Build the Unknown

BUILD THE

W · W · NORTON & COMPANY · INC · *New York*

UNKNOWN

HOW SCIENTISTS CREATE THE MATERIALS OF TOMORROW FOR THE DESIGNS OF TODAY

By Irwin Stambler

ILLUSTRATED WITH PHOTOGRAPHS

To David and Ethel Lebowitz

CONTENTS

Books by Irwin Stambler

Find a Career in Aviation
Space Ship: The Story of the X-15
Wonders of Underwater Exploration
Breath of Life

With Gordon Ashmead

Find a Career in Engineering

ACKNOWLEDGMENTS

The title of this book, *Build the Unknown*, highlights the revolutionary changes taking place in the sometimes unheralded realm of materials. An author, too, must build his manuscript up, hopefully on a solid foundation, yet of somewhat more insubstantial building materials than are described further on in these pages.

I have been fortunate in having the assistance of many individuals and companies in putting together the new story of the birth of materials science. Among those scientific organizations to whom I am indebted are Battelle Memorial Institute, Stanford Research Institute, University of California at Los Angeles, MIT, Atomic Energy Commission, National Aeronautics and Space Administration, and Armour Research Institute. I would like to thank Bill Kinner and Alcoa for providing much information, including a copy of "Alcoa, An American Enterprise," by Charles C. Carr (Rinehart

& Co., New York, 1952). U.S. Steel's "The Making, Shaping and Treating of Steel," Seventh Edition, 1957 (© U.S. Steel) was invaluable. I would also like to thank Ed Egan of U.S. Steel, Dudley Ross of Kaiser Aluminum and Brent Breedin of E. I. Du Pont de Nemours & Co. I am also grateful for the aid of the following organizations: General Electric Research Laboratories; Atomics International; Dow Chemical Company and Dow Magnesium; Ford Motor Company and Ford Aeronutronics Division; Manufacturing Chemists' Association (and the Chemical Industry Facts Book); American Ceramic Society; Society of the Plastics Industry; Autonetics Division of North American Aviation; Hughes Tool Company; Union Carbide; Westinghouse Electric; Carborundum Corporation; and the Corning Glass Corporation.

Build the Unknown

1

THE MATERIALS
REVOLUTION

SCIENTISTS OF TODAY are challenged to find the solutions for two widely different problems. On the one hand they are seeking ways to explore the vast distances of space, to reach the planets, and to push outward toward the beckoning stars. This is perhaps the most exciting field of study. Certainly it is the best publicized. At the same time, a much less glamorous area of research is of even greater personal importance to most of us who will remain earthbound homebodies for our entire lives. Here on earth we still face the ancient problems of disease, poverty, and ignorance. It probably will be harder to free the world from hunger than it will be to put a research station on a moon of Jupiter.

Man's ambitions to reach the worlds in space and change the world at home may very well hinge on what is happening in a new field of study called the science of materials. Researchers in this new science work with particles of matter so tiny that they cannot be seen under the most powerful microscope. Scientists are learning to understand, reorganize, and change these particles in the basic structure of matter to produce new and infinitely better materials.

Better materials, in turn, will enable us to make use of incredibly great sources of power, explore space, improve medicine, reclaim huge areas of land for farming, increase the output of present farms, improve transportation and communication, and make possible hundreds of inventions which will add to the comfort of all of us. Just as the stone implements of prehistoric man were replaced by tools of metals, we will find the materials of the world we know outmoded by substances familiar at the present time to only a handful of scientists.

Already there have been so many changes in the field of materials that scientists say we are having a materials revolution. Less than a century ago man had a few metals, some chemicals, and a number of natural materials such as wood, animal hair, and plant fibers. In the past fifty to seventy-five years and particularly in the last five to ten years the list of materials has doubled and redoubled. In the past decade man has gone beyond the use of only those materials available in nature and has begun to make completely new substances. These synthetic materials, such as the hundreds of different plastics in use today, have been created in the laboratory by the forced and sometimes lucky combination of different elements.

Most of the new synthetics were made by the trial and error method. Batches of different materials were mixed together until new materials with different properties were found. The next step in materials science is to go beyond the time-wasting trial and error method and tailor materials to meet various needs. Included in this approach will be new ways of mixing elements and, more important, applying great amounts of energy to create new elements. These man-made elements will then become special materials for special jobs.

To understand these staggering claims for the new science, we must first know what is meant by the word "material." Webster says the word means "of or pertaining to or consisting of matter." Every physical substance is composed of matter. Everything in this world including our own bodies is made of matter. For purposes of this book, we will use the more common definition of materials as things outside our bodies. In most cases, when we speak of materials, we mean the things around us which we can use, touch, see, taste, or smell.

As we have said, all materials are composed of matter, and scientists have discovered that there is a great similarity in all forms of matter. All matter is made up of tiny particles called atoms. Each atom, in turn, is made up of a central nucleus around which orbit even smaller particles called electrons.

The simplest form of matter is called an element. An element is any substance which cannot be separated into other substances by ordinary chemical means; that is, its atoms must be torn apart by some special process or device such as an "atom smasher."

Scientists also found that there were some ninety-two different elements found in nature. The names of these basic elements are given in the glossary (page 184) and include such things as oxygen, iron, helium, hydrogen, and aluminum. These elements are all made up of atoms having nuclei and electrons, yet they obviously look different and have different properties. What, then, makes this difference? Scientists, after hundreds of years of study, finally concluded that the properties of each different element depend on the number of electrons circling each nucleus. For instance, the basic hydrogen atom consists of the nucleus plus one electron orbiting it. Copper has twenty-nine electrons arranged in four successive orbital "shells." (A group of electrons whose orbits all are about the same distance away from the nucleus is called a shell.) Similarly, aluminum has thirteen electrons in three shells, carbon six in two shells, silicon fourteen in three shells, and so on.

If enough force is applied, the outermost electrons in some of the shells can be torn out of their orbit. This is the basic principle used in all electronic and electrical circuits. This property of materials can be used to set up a flow of electrons either in gases or in solid materials to give electric current. It is fairly easy to do this, but it's a different thing to break apart the inside structure of an atom. Great forces are needed to do this. But in the past few years man has learned how to generate these forces to produce nuclear energy.

Each atomic system has its own internal forces. We might compare such forces to the gravitational forces that keep man from falling off the earth and the many other forces that keep the earth, Venus, the sun and other parts of our solar system travelling in their year-round paths. Such forces vary somewhat from atom to atom. The study of these and other forces — generated, for instance, when an electron is broken away from one atom or shared between two atoms — forms the basis for much of today's materials technology.

Because of such effects, for instance, billions of atoms (and it should be noted that atoms are so small no human has ever directly seen one) can bond together to form large pieces of materials we know as a metal, plastic, or some other substance. It is also thanks to this that different elements can be combined to form new materials with properties different from the various elements that make it up. For example, consider the elements magnesium and oxygen. By themselves, magnesium is a bendable metal and oxygen a colorless gas. But the two combine to form magnesium oxide. Magnesium oxide is neither a metal nor a gas, but a hard and brittle ceramic.

Until now, man had to accept the ninety-two natural elements and go from there. He could merge them in various ways to form new materials, but he had little control over the way the basic elements lined themselves up in such "mergers." The growth of materials science is slowly changing this. Now we are finding out how to manipulate the basic atomic struture.

We are learning more about the forces that hold the atom together, the forces that keep the electrons orbiting around the nucleus. As we find out about these forces, we can predict, for example, what will happen if there is a drastic change in the distance of an electron from the nucleus of an atom. Once our predictions are accurate, we can force the electrons into different patterns to create an element with properties necessary for a particular purpose. No longer will it be necessary to simply accept the properties of a material and adjust a design accordingly. Designs can be made to fit a certain need and materials created to fit the design.

On a different level, the study of the interaction of atoms with each other and then the relationships of large groups of atoms to other large groups of atoms is also being undertaken. In this area, scientists have found that by changing the way in which atoms are arranged, or by controlling the way crystals of various materials are formed, they can vastly improve material properties.

So it is that we are on the threshold of a brand new "Age." The editor of the magazine "Materials in Design Engineering," H. R. Clauser, has pointed out, "Three of the eras in man's past history have been designated the Stone Age, the Bronze Age and the Iron Age. They were thus named because the civilization of each of them was dominated by and dependent on one material. Now again, in this present century, materials have assumed a position of pre-eminence. They are perhaps the most important single factor on which the advance of our technology depends."

To realize the vital importance of materials to today's modern society, we have only to glance at the role of a basic industry such as steel manufacturing. For one thing, this is one of the most important sources of employment in the United States. Nearly three quarters of a million people work in the steel manufacturing plants alone. To this can be added hundreds of thousands of others working in jobs which depend on the steel industry. In 1960, this country produced about 1,100 tons of steel for every person living in our land. By contrast, the rest of the world turned out only about 200 tons per person. Most of this production was in countries as highly developed as the nations of Europe and, in the Far East, Japan.

This clearly indicates that materials play a major role in making the living standard in the United States the highest in the world. It is no accident that underdeveloped nations of the world, as soon as they achieve their independence, immediately make plans for establishing steel-making industries inside their borders. You might think that this could flood the world's markets in coming years with more steel than could be used. Certainly with many other new materials being developed, it might be thought that this would be even more likely to be the case.

But all signs indicate just the opposite. The more the people of the world increase their living standards, the more materials of all kinds are needed. It has been noted that all the other countries produce at least 900 tons of steel per person per year less than the amount produced in the United States. If all the other lands were to come up to our standard, states M. A. Scheil, Director of Metallurgical Research for the A. O. Smith Company, it would require one billion, 250 million ingot tons of steel. In the early 1960s, total world production of steel came to only 381 million tons, less than a third of what would be needed for worldwide high living standards. The planned world capacity by the late '60s of 571 million tons still falls far short of the goal.

Looking beyond steel, industry by industry we can see the impact of materials build-up. Aluminum, copper, chemicals, mining, and dozens of other basic materials fields employ millions upon millions of people. Many of these industries were virtually nonexistent a few decades ago. Looking ahead, we can already see brand new materials industries ready to come into being — nuclear materials, radiation chemistry, very low temperature technology, to name a few. And who knows what radical changes in our approach to materials may come about from what we find on other planets once space travel becomes commonplace.

Some of the trends in the materials revolution can be seen in the automobile. As Scheil notes, in 1910 eleven standard kinds of steel were used in automobiles. Today, the car in your driveway contains no less than 162 different kinds of steel, not to speak of other metals, such as aluminum and bronze, as well as various types of plastics.

"The late 19th century," says H. R. Clauser, "and the beginning of the current one saw the birth of the new age of materials. Steel became the major material of engineering, aluminum a commercial metal, Hyatt invented Celluloid, and Baekeland developed Bakelite."

As shall be seen in succeeding pages, the ranks of important engineering materials since 1900 have expanded and expanded again. To the above names, we can add tantalum, beryllium, aluminum oxide, praesodymium, berkelium, epoxy resins, and countless others. In the future, materials scientists will unify all materials into a single materials technology. Thus the new materials age is no longer dominated by just one material as in past periods in history. It deals with all of them and will undoubtedly be called by historians of the future the "Materials Age."

2

THE FIRST
MATERIALS

FOR THOUSANDS AND thousands of years, animal skins, bone, wood, and stones were all the materials man knew. Of course, over the centuries, man managed to make a number of very useful tools from stone. He first chipped out stone axes, arrowheads, and spear points. As time went on, he progressed to more and more complex tools, such as awls, knives, and harpoons. Stone has provided most of man's durable tools for most of his existence on earth. It is only in comparatively recent times that man discovered metals.

The first stone tools apparently were used by human beings some 700,000 years ago. This period of stone tools, called the Stone Age, lasted for hundreds of thousands of years. It is only about 10,000 years ago that the Stone Age came to a close. All the while that man chopped down trees with stone axes or fished with hooks made from bone, the harder, more durable materials that could make him ruler of this planet lay all around him, but he didn't realize it.

These materials—metals and chemicals—were locked in the ground in earth, mud, and rocks. Just about all the elements in nature exist in combination with other elements. In such combinations, the advantages of a particular element often are masked by the much poorer properties of the combined substance. To primitive man, a lump of material containing iron or copper looked just like a different colored rock. Indeed, it was rock (such metal-containing rocks are called ores) and the unwanted parts of it had to be taken away to free the useful metal.

Those metals not hidden from sight in ores or mixed in with clay or dirt were gold, silver, and particularly important, copper. Such metals sometimes can be found in a fairly pure metallic state in the form of nuggets. In some places, these nuggets existed on the surface of the earth or not too far from the surface. Gold, in the form of ornaments, probably was the first metal used by ancient people.

Not too long after, sometime in the late stretches of the Stone Age, some men stumbled upon nuggets of copper. They were probably attracted by the different color and perhaps the reddish-brown shine. At first, these nuggets were used for ornaments. Then one of the more advanced thinkers of that day found that the nuggets could be hammered into shapes. A little later in history, it was deduced that melting a number of the nuggets in a pot, then cooling this melt could provide a big slab of metal. The larger piece could then be

hammered into such things as swords or shields. Usually it wasn't pure copper that was worked, but a mixture
of copper and some other metal. In particular, copper
combined with tin provided an alloy called bronze.
Copper mixed with zinc formed an alloy we now call
brass.

The period when copper and its alloys were the main
metals used is called the Bronze Age. Considering the
long time span of the Stone Age, the Bronze Age is
almost modern. Probably the wide-spread use of such
metals started somewhere about 5000 B.C. Archaeologists can only estimate the date, but they are fairly
certain that methods of working copper and other
metals originated in southwestern Asia. It spread slowly
to other parts of the world. Evidence indicates the
Bronze Age began in Greece and Crete around 3000
B.C. By about 1500 B.C., a lively trade existed throughout Europe in raw copper and bronze or in tools and
weapons made of these metals. During this period,
several other metals — silver, lead, and tin — were
discovered.

In the meantime, progress was going on over these
centuries in materials for building, for storing and carrying food, and for clothing. Man undoubtedly learned
how to braid plant leaves, grasses, and other vegetable
materials into clothing and baskets long before 5000
B.C. Also before this time, man began building houses
of dried mud brick. Sometime after 5000 B.C. he learned
the art of making pottery.

Exactly how people discovered the connection between clay and fire to make ceramics is lost in the haze of time. One possibility is that a tribesman might have been making figures or forms of clay near a fire. Somehow the part may have ended up in the fire. Later, the artist might have been surprised to find a smooth, hard object much stronger than ordinary clay in the ashes of the fire.

After 3000 B.C., we know from archaeological finds, the art of pottery-making was highly advanced. By 1-2000 B.C., skilled craftsmen in Greece, Egypt, and Asia turned out all kinds of bowls, pitchers, and other items. Included among these are many magnificently formed and painted art treasures that can be found in museums throughout the world.

A near relation to pottery-making is glass-making. Some of the sources of glass materials, for instance, are certain types of clay. The earliest glass we know of was found in the form of glass beads in an Egyptian tomb of about 2500 B.C. A small green glass rod found in Eshnunna, Babylonia, may even be a century older. The Egyptians from 1500 down to perhaps 1000 B.C. made a great many glass objects, remains of which have been found in many places. The Roman Empire had a great glass industry with bowls, dishes, and other eating utensils made of this material. Archaeologists have even found that widespread packaging of goods in small glass containers was done in the days of the Romans. Glass remains indicate that much of the work of those days was of beautiful design — cut glass, gold leaf inserts, and other decorative effects. So great was the volume of glass used in Rome that only in the past few hundred years has the amount of glass usage surpassed it.

Also about 5000 B.C. man made another major step forward in materials. He began to use textiles. Instead of using the skins stripped from animals for clothing, floor coverings, and bedding, man discovered how to take fiber from certain plants or the wool from sheep and weave it on a loom. There are two opposing theories as to when and where this took place. One group of scientists believes weaving began in Mesopotamia (now called Iraq) and spread from there throughout the world. Others think weaving probably was invented in several different places in the world at about the same time and without contact between the various inventors.

Naturally, since textiles are far more perishable than metals, wood, or ceramics, very little of the work of the ancients has come down to us. However, from sculptures and Egyptian paintings we can see that by 3000 to 1500 B.C., textiles of many hues and in beautiful forms were being created.

Clay cuneiform tablets found at the ancient city of Ur (a city of ancient Sumeria, located in what is now southern Iraq) dating from about 2200 B.C. have references to weavers and weaving. Excavations at Mohenjo-Daro in India turned up bits of cotton cloth preserved in association with copper dating back 3000 years. Carved wood and clay models found in Egyptian tombs and now displayed in the Metropolitan Museum in New York show weavers spinning thread, then weaving it into cloth.

Plant fibers such as tree bark and coconut husks probably were first used by man for textiles, followed soon after by wool from sheep. Other animal fibers used included camel hair and goat and horse hair. It has been established that linen cloth was made from flax in Egypt before 4000 B.C. In fact, archaeologists have found linen cloth finer than any made today. For instance, Verla Birrell, Assistant Professor of Art in Home Economics, University of Utah, reports that one such piece was found to have 540 threads to the inch with a width of sixty inches and length of over six yards.

Wars have been fought over materials. In early days, nations often set up elaborate security systems to keep to themselves methods of making certain kinds of materials. Perhaps the prime example is that of silk.

Silk, which comes from the cocoons woven by silkworms, is thought to have been invented in China before 2600 B.C. The secret was kept, under penalty of death for disclosure, for thousands of years. Finally, neighboring nations managed to bribe or lure away some Chinese who knew the process. In 300 A.D., Japan learned from four Chinese girls who accompanied some Koreans to Japan about how to raise silkworms on a diet of mulberry tree leaves. Silk culture was introduced into India, according to one story, by a Chinese princess who carried silkworm eggs and mulberry tree seeds hidden in the lining of her headdress.

Alexander the Great brought word, but not knowledge, of the process to Greece after his invasion of India. Silk production was not introduced to the West until 550 A.D. This was done when Emperor Justinian of the Byzantine Empire met two Persian monks in Constantinople (now Istanbul, Turkey). The monks had lived long in China and knew how silk was made. They were talked into returning to China and smuggling out silkworm eggs. They did this by hiding the eggs inside a hollow cane. All the succeeding silk production of Europe sprang from these few eggs.

Even then, the process was not disclosed to the people of Europe proper. It was not until about 827 A.D. that Saracen weavers brought silk production to Sicily. Later movements of heirs of these weavers, because of wars and invasions, finally spread silk production to Italy. From there, it slowly spread to the rest of Europe, reaching Tours about 1480 and England about 1585. The first appearance of silk-making in the new world was in Mexico in 1522, when Cortes ordered an official to import silkworms for this.

The use of bronze, the discovery of textiles, and pottery-making all led to a flowering of civilization. Great cities arose in the valley of the Euphrates and Tigris. In the valley of the Nile, the great power that was Egypt came into being, while at the same time, China rose to prominence on the other side of the world. Man was now ready for the next major step forward in his mastery of materials.

The title given to this period is the Iron Age. It started sometime after 1600 B.C. This does not mean that iron was unknown before this. In fact, pieces of iron were found in some of the very earliest Egyptian monuments thus far excavated. One such is from the Great Pyramid built about 2900 B.C. An even earlier find of what appears to be an iron dagger was made by archaeologists digging at the site of the Sumerian city Ur of the Chaldees. This implement dates back to about 3100 B.C.

However, though iron was known that far back, most experts doubt that the people of that period actually knew how to extract iron from its ores. Unlike copper, very little iron existed in the almost pure metallic state. There was one exception: meteorites which had plunged through earth's atmosphere from outer space. The tremendous heat to which the meteorites were subjected on hitting the atmosphere burned out the impurities. This left lumps of iron which plummeted down to earth.

Thus it's believed that most iron used by man before about 2000 B.C. came from meteorites. This belief seems strengthened by the names given iron by ancient peoples. Most of these names translated into English come out in such forms as "stone from heaven" or "star metal." Iron from meteorites found today contains about the same amount of nickel (seven to fifteen per cent) as that discovered in the iron relics from ancient tombs. This again seems to verify the theory that iron was a rare, probably very precious, metal during the Bronze Age.

The bulk of the iron on earth's surface is in combination with rock or earth and would certainly look unpromising to someone not familiar with iron metallurgy. Thus it was no easy thing for early man to find out how to make iron. It probably took some form of accidental discovery to lead man to this vital material. It's been suggested that men may have built fires on hearths made of iron-bearing rocks. Under just the right conditions, pure iron could be left after the other elements had been burned or reacted off. (These "right conditions" were first that a strong, natural draft was needed to provide a very high temperature. After this high temperature was obtained, the iron ore had to be in close contact with the hot coals in such a way that air was excluded.)

This alone was not enough, for the resulting iron would still be full of air holes and pockets of impurities. In this state, iron is called "sponge." Somewhere along the line, someone had to realize that hammering the iron in the red hot stage would drive out the impurities, called slag, and leave a strong piece of metal. One of the first peoples to find out how to do this lived in what is now India. They produced a form of steel called wootz. Exactly when this was first done is still being argued by experts. Some insist it goes back before 2000 B.C. Others say it probably occurred later than this. At any rate, by 1350 to 1100 B.C., iron making had spread throughout most of the countries in the Middle East.

The Greeks made little use of iron. The Romans, on the other hand, mastered the art of iron-making, improved on it, and used the metal widely. In particular, the great power of the Roman legions, which made Rome ruler of the world, was based on their metal armament which was much more efficient than anything known before. As Rome took over all of what is now Europe, her smiths introduced methods of extracting and working iron and other metals.

The use of iron and steel transformed the face of the world and was the final link in the chain making man overlord of the earth. Not only did the Romans have steel swords, metal breastplates, and shields, they also used metal plows to improve farming. Steel razors, stone-cutting tools, files, and surgical instruments were just a few of the other uses of the metal in the centuries just before and after the birth of Christ.

It might be surprising to think of steel, which we often consider a strictly modern material, as being that widely used so long ago. Even extra-strong tempered steel was apparently known. A steel chisel with a hardened point, believed to be nearly 2500 years old, was found in an ancient city of Ceylon.

Basically, the difference between iron and steel is that steel is iron containing small amounts of carbon — usually under two per cent. The properties of iron can be changed greatly depending on the per cent of carbon it contains. Too much carbon in the iron causes it to be very brittle. But some carbon is needed, for without it the iron is too soft and weak. Of course, modern-day steel, which is superior to that of the ancient world, also includes carefully added amounts of other alloying elements besides carbon.

Iron smelted from iron ore picks up a certain amount of carbon from the hot coals used in the process. This iron can be cast or hammered into shapes. (In ancient times, though, it would appear that people did not know how to properly cast iron.) A cast iron part keeps a lot of this carbon which makes it brittle. A sharp blow, for instance, might break such a part. A wrought iron part made by hammering or by applying a great amount of pressure to hot iron, will have much less carbon than cast iron, since the pressure forces out much of the impurities. In fact, so much of the carbon is forced out that almost pure iron remains. Wrought parts aren't brittle, but they are much softer than cast iron.

By adding some carbon to the wrought product, the much stronger material called steel is made. Steel, of course, can take a lot of punishment. If it's hit sharply, it usually springs back to its original shape.

Most of the iron used from 1350 B.C. to 1300 A.D., though, was in wrought form. Steel was more expensive and not too much was produced. Still, in the time of the Roman Empire, man did know how to add just the small per cent of carbon needed to make steel. Until the 1800s, when a breakthrough invented by Henry Bessemer changed things, there were only two ways to do this and both were known by the Romans. These were the cementation and crucible processes.

In the first, the carbon content of wrought iron was increased by placing it in contact with hot carbon. The second method involved heating the wrought iron in contact with special clay crucibles. The crucibles contained carbon that was given up to the iron. But during the "Dark Ages" both these methods were lost and man had to use iron in wrought or cast form. The cementation method was re-invented in Belgium in 1600 A.D. and the crucible process in England by Benjamin Huntsman in 1742.

We can see, therefore, that man had reached a fairly high level of materials development at the peak of Roman power. Iron, steel, and bronze, intricately woven textiles, stone, marble, and wood let man build impressive cities and broad highways. The Roman roads were so well built that many stretches of them are still usable today. Metal chariots as well as peasant carts carried food and other goods up and down most of Europe. In other parts of the world, which had almost no contact with Europe and the Middle East, similar progress was made. Chinese civilization produced everything from rockets to writing paper, beautiful bronze vases, and eating utensils. In the new world, the Indian civilizations of South and Central America were also building huge cities with many-tiered stone ceremonial buildings and broad plazas. Many of these cities were also connected by paved highways hundreds of miles long.

A few centuries after Christ, the roster of materials came to a stop. The last major metal found in ancient times was mercury, which began to be used about 500 to 700 B.C. The list of six or eight metals known to man in the days of the Roman empire was not increased for

33

over 2,000 years. After the discovery of mercury, no metal was recognized until platinum was added to the roster in 1525 A.D. Any advances made during this period were based mainly on refinements of already known materials. Some of the present-day exotic materials, such as tungsten and molybdenum, were known to some scientists, but they were mainly curiosities. Little or nothing was done with them. In many cases, over the period from the fall of the Roman Empire to the scientific renaissance of the 17th and 18th centuries, man's knowledge of materials actually lessened rather than increased. An example given earlier was the loss in Europe of the knowledge of how to make steel.

In textiles, the Romans brought Greek, Egyptian, and other skilled weavers to Rome and, using knowledge gained from them, set up textile centers throughout their empire. Progress in turning out more intricate types of cloth continued throughout the Roman era. After Rome fell, cloth was still made, but it tended to be just a few kinds of relatively rough material. By the Middle Ages, much of the cloth turned out in Europe was a coarse wool called Burre that was widely used by the average man.

The feudal lords, if they wanted elaborate clothing or tapestries, had to import them from the countries of the Middle East and Asia. The artisans of Persia, China and India, though not improving their manufacturing methods much over ancient times, turned out ever more impressive textiles with brilliant colors and interesting patterns. In the Western Hemisphere, completely independent of Europe and Asia, the Incas and their predecessors learned just about all known weaving methods and turned out magnificent works of art, some of which can be seen today in museums.

As far as Europe was concerned, it was not until the Crusades re-established direct contact with the Near East that advances in textiles came about. After about 1300 A.D., the background gained from the Crusades led to the formation of groups of skilled weavers in Italy. This experience slowly spread from Italy throughout Europe. Eventually it formed the base from which the textile industry of the American colonies sprang.

In all areas of materials the world over, one pattern held true. No matter how advanced the type of material turned out, whether metal, ceramic, or textile, production was almost always a family affair. The materials usually were made in small amounts in what were essentially hand operations. The first great step forward in materials production know-how was the Industrial Revolution.

3

METALS TODAY

TODAY'S RAPID TRANSPORTATION systems and the many comforts we now use each day began to develop during the Industrial Revolution. For thousands of years, goods and products were turned out bit-by-bit in family-style home factories. Then, in the course of a few hundred years, the expansion of technology led to what we now know as mass production. The "muscle" for the Industrial Revolution was a mighty metal that gave its name to the last major materials age — iron, and its alloy, steel. These metals aided the rapid growth of knowledge which, in turn, led to the development of aluminum, magnesium, and the "light metals age." Iron, steel, aluminum, and magnesium (plus that old standby copper and its alloys) are the basic metals of today's scientific age.

The railroads were pushed across the United States. Without them, much of the West might still be wilderness populated mainly by Indians. The train wheels

The stainless-steel-domed Civic Arena, Pittsburgh, Pennsylvania.

clacked across mile after mile of track made of ribbons of steel. The puffing steam engine itself was a symbol of this strong material, for it was nicknamed "the iron horse." The slow, awkward galleons of Spain and the later and swifter Yankee Clippers of the age of wood and sail gave way to the steel deck plates of the ocean liner and the workhorse freighter.

This material that answered the needs of the Industrial Revolution was one, as we've seen, that had been used for centuries before. The difference was that ways had been found to turn out iron and steel in very large quantities. If these breakthroughs had not been achieved, there would be no modern civilization. Millions of tons of steel are needed each year to make trucks and automobiles. The large apartment buildings and great skyscrapers that are the mark of today's major cities depend for their strength on steel girders. Steel beams and cables make possible the great bridges that span some of the world's mightiest rivers.

More important, the parts used in the huge manufacturing equipment of basic industry are made of iron and steel. All kinds of heavy machine tools, from lathes to great stamping presses, are the basis of all modern production. These tools are used to shape and work just about all other materials, both metal and non-metal. These basic tools must be made from iron and steel, or in most cases they would not be strong enough to do the job.

Multiply these few examples by thousands of other vital uses and you have some idea of how much depends on a large supply of iron and steel.

From the fall of the Roman Empire to almost modern times, there was little advancement in the art of steelmaking. There is, however, one major exception — the blast furnace. This was the first step towards production of iron and steel in large amounts. Today at steel plants throughout the world, the huge blast furnaces — naturally many times the size of the early, crude designs — work round the clock as integral parts of the iron and steel industry.

The original blast furnace was developed by ironmakers of central Europe about 1350 A.D. Before this invention, there really was no such thing as cast iron. Iron was made by placing iron ore and charcoal on a crude hearth and letting air enter the hearth through a duct at the bottom of the furnace. The reaction of air, charcoal, and ore removed impurities to leave sponge iron from which wrought iron was made. However, the temperature wasn't high enough to make the iron liquid so it could be poured.

For a long time, the furnace would always be built so the air inlet faced a direction from which a strong wind usually was blowing. The air, in effect, was used to "fan the flames" of a charcoal fire. If some way could be found to move the air into the hearth faster, iron-makers came to realize, then hotter temperatures could be gained. Hotter temperatures meant that iron could be brought to a molten state in the furnace and could then be poured, or cast, into molds.

The answer to the problem was the blast furnace in which a blast of air was sent into the hearth by mechanical means. In early designs, this was done by men blowing through hollow reeds or pumping air from bellows of animal skins. Later air-blowing devices were operated by water wheels, and eventually engine-driven air pumps were used. As recently as the middle 1800s, the output of the average blast furnace was only one to six tons of "pig" iron a day. (Slabs of this cast iron are called "pigs.") By 1880, this had finally been upped to 100 tons per day, and today vastly more efficient furnaces turn out over 1600 tons of pig iron a day.

The great volume of pig iron that can be made by the blast furnace provides the large amounts of iron needed to have large-scale steel production. For most of recorded history there were only two ways of making steel from iron, both of which were lost for centuries and rediscovered only after 1600. Both these methods, though, are slow and time-consuming. Steel could be made, but it was relatively expensive and not enough could be turned out to meet the rapidly expanding needs of the Industrial Revolution. It took another great achievement to make steel the kingpin of basic industry. This was the Bessemer Converter.

The Bessemer Converter is named after Sir Henry Bessemer of England. It could just as well have been called the Kelly Converter. William Kelly of Kentucky and Bessemer, after years of study, both arrived at the same general process without either being aware the other was working on it. Bessemer applied for and was granted an American patent in 1856, a year ahead of Kelly's application. Kelly, though, proved he had been working on his own version since 1847 and also won a patent. But since Bessemer's work was made public first, his name has ever since been connected with the method.

The process makes use of a device that looks roughly like a huge oldtime cannon with its muzzle pointed upwards. This metal shell can be tilted over either to receive a charge of molten pig iron or to pour out molten steel. The device is called a converter because it is used to convert the pig iron directly into steel while in the liquid state. The heart of the method was based on Kelly's and Bessemer's discovery that a great amount of heat is generated by reaction of cold air with impurities in the red hot iron. Thus by just sending blasts of cold air up through the bottom or sides of the converter and through the liquid iron, enough heat was automatically generated to burn off undesired impurities and leave the right amount of carbon to provide steel. The liquid steel could then be poured out into molds. Using cold air and not having to heat the converter by external devices made this a quick, relatively simple way to make large amounts of steel.

Of course, though the basic method is simple, it still took a great amount of effort and heartbreak before success was gained. Bessemer made good steel from some types of ores, but it soon turned out that the process didn't work with other types. So-called low-grade ores which contained a lot of phosphorus, for instance, resulted in very poor quality steel. Then it turned out that even high-grade Swedish pig iron didn't come out right. It contained too much oxygen and went bad in the molds. Bessemer held to his idea and examined dozens of possible materials which could be added to the iron to solve the problem. He finally found a certain type of material called *speigeleisen*, which included manganese and carbon. Adding this to the Swedish iron took up the extra oxygen while also combining with other impurities. These combinations then floated to the surface of the converter melt in the form of a scum that could be skimmed off. By 1871, the process began to be generally accepted. From then on, more and more steel was made in Bessemer Converters until, by 1910, this was the most used steelmaking process in the world.

Still, the Bessemer way left much to be desired. In particular, it still was not much good with high-phosphorus ores. As time went on, more and more high-grade ores were used up, leaving vast deposits of low-grade ores as the main remaining supply. At the same time, the demand for steel continued to skyrocket. So again inventors throughout the world tried to think up other production methods.

Dozens of these were proposed, but none worked out until Karl Wilhelm Siemens, born in Germany but a naturalized English citizen, proved his open hearth invention would meet the test. His solution was to put pig iron, or pig iron plus iron scrap, in a rectangular, covered hearth. Then hot fuel gas plus air was introduced at both ends of the furnace and the mixture ignited. The tremendous heat generated caused chemical reaction with the iron, and the final result was steel. The open hearth method was particularly important in the United States. It worked with high-phosphorus as well as other types of iron ores, and the United States had large reserves of high-phosphorus iron. Another advantage was that the open hearth method permitted much closer control of the amount of carbon and other alloying elements that give different steels different properties. Today, nearly ninety per cent — over eighty million tons — of the steel made in the United States each year is produced by open hearth furnaces. Bessemer's method is still used, but only for about two or three per cent of our national production.

Each of these giant furnaces can make about 300 tons of steel at one time. In this picture are seen the charging machine used for adding scrap and other materials, and in the background a ladle making a hot-metal addition — molten iron.

The finishing temperature of open-hearth steel is in the neighborhood of 3,000 degrees Fahrenheit, varying according to the composition and grade of the steel. Shown here is a "heat" of steel being "jet tapped." In the "jet tapping" process, an explosive charge is set off in the tapping hole of the open-hearth furnace.

The next major process was developed by Paul L. T. Heroult of France and used electricity. Called the electric arc furnace, it was first successfully used in 1899. Heroult inserted several electrodes into a furnace containing iron. By arcing current between the electrodes, a great amount of heat was provided to burn out the impurities and leave steel. This approach accounts for about twice the amount of steel made by the Bessemer process in today's production, but it still ranks far below the open hearth.

However, the electric arc makes possible even closer control of alloying elements in steel. Thus some steels made in this way have special properties for such things as advanced aircraft and spacecraft. It was found recently that arc-melting and alloying certain kinds of steels in furnaces surrounded by vacuums provided super-pure steels. These have much higher strengths than if the same materials were made in furnaces open to the air. The reason for this is that drawing a vacuum removes a small amount of harmful elements floating in the air. During conventional non-vacuum melting, these elements get into the steel to lower its final strength.

All these advanced methods of the past seventy-five to 100 years made it possible to turn out great amounts of steel. Of course, when we talk of steel, we really refer to many, many different materials. By changing the percentage of any one of a dozen or more metals contained in the steel, we can provide an almost infinite variety of steels. Thus there are high carbon steels, low carbon steels, ductile steels for springs, magnetic steels, very high temperature steels for spacecraft skins — the list is almost endless. The new types of furnaces made much of this possible by permitting very precise control of alloying.

Apart from steel, these furnaces or modifications of them permit making many other combinations of iron with various metals. For instance, one series is called nickel-base alloys, another cobalt-base. By having perhaps forty to fifty per cent cobalt or nickel combined with up to thirty per cent iron, plus small percentages of other alloying elements, a whole range of alloys known as superalloys have been made. These superalloys are much more expensive than regular grades of steel, but they also can do jobs steel can't. A prime example of this is the famed X-15 research plane. This plane travels out into space and then returns into the atmosphere so fast that its wing leading edges and nose skins turn cherry red from friction with the air. Although material temperature goes well over 1000 degrees, no failure occurs. The superalloy used for these vital parts and for all skin of the X-15 is a nickel-base one called Inconel X. The successor to the X-15, the Dyna-Soar, will orbit the earth before re-entering the atmosphere and will face even more severe heating. Dyna-Soar will have a nickel-base alloy skin. As a last example, it can be noted that the shingled skins on the outside of the Mercury capsule that protected astronauts Shepard, Grissom, Glenn, Carpenter, and Schirra were made mainly of cobalt-base alloys.

Steels of all kinds, certain types of iron, and superalloys are all major metals of today. In fact, steel is still the number one metal on which present day civilization depends. But since the turn of the century, a new series of metals has come along to change radically the world as we know it. They are the light metals, aluminum and magnesium alloys. If the 1800s and the first few decades of this century could be called the age of steel, the past ten or twenty years might be dubbed the light metals age.

Aluminum was one of the last of the more widely used metals of today to be discovered. Actually, in its main combined form, aluminum oxide, it has been used for thousands of years. (Aluminum oxide is made of aluminum mated with oxygen. This combination provides a ceramic material.) Aluminum is one of the most abundant elements on earth. In combined form, it appears in just about every rock, every bush and tree, most forms of clay, and even in most animals. Many of the pieces of pottery made in ancient times were formed from aluminum-bearing clay. However, it was not until 1807 that the great English scientist

Most metals are obtained from raw "ores" mined out of the ground. Here aluminum ore (bauxite) is mined from surface deposits in Surinam, South America.

Alcoa

Sir Humphrey Davy suggested that the ceramic aluminum oxide might contain a new metal.

Davy wasn't able to separate it, though. This was finally done by Danish scientist Hans Christian Oersted in 1825. Oersted did it by causing a chemical reaction between a purified compound of aluminum, anhydrous aluminum chloride, and dilute potassium amalgam. He was able to obtain only a very small residue of metal this way. Finally, in 1854, the French researcher Henri Sainte Claire Deville used sodium instead of the more expensive potassium and produced a sizable piece of aluminum. In the Paris Exposition of 1855, he exhibited the first solid bar of the metal ever seen by the public. The amazing lightness and strength of the bar made many who saw or heard about this exhibit realize the great potential of producing aluminum in large amounts. A light, strong, ductile material such as this could make possible vehicles many times more efficient than those made of heavier materials such as steel. Many things never before possible in engineering might be achieved with such a metal.

Scientists and inventors in many different countries set to the task of trying to mass-produce aluminum. Soon some ways were suggested and some even patented, but they were all too slow, too hard to accomplish or, more important, far too expensive. The answer, when it came, arrived not from a well-staffed laboratory or from the work of a well-known scientist at a leading university, but from a woodshed in a small town in Ohio in 1885.

The man who solved the problem was Charles Martin Hall. He was twenty-two years old and had just recently graduated from Oberlin College. Strangely enough, just as in the case of Bessemer and Kelly, he was not alone in finding a solution. A French metallurgist, Paul L. T. Heroult, developed the same general method completely on his own. However, Heroult did not realize the worth of his invention right away and did not try to commercialize it until after Hall had laid the groundwork for what is now the Aluminum Company of America (Alcoa). In keeping with the saw about fact being stranger than fiction, the lives of these two were surprisingly parallel. Heroult was also twenty-two when he found out how to make aluminum, and both Heroult and Hall died in 1914. Heroult, of course, achieved fame later as the inventor of the electric arc furnace for steelmaking.

Hall became interested in aluminum in college. In chemistry classes with the famed Professor F. F. Jewett, he heard of Sainte Claire Deville's work in France. He became obsessed with the idea of finding a cheap way to extract aluminum from its ores, primarily the main ore, which is called bauxite. One method of separating metals from their ores was to pass an electric current through a metal. It had been used many times on a limited laboratory basis for other kinds of metals as well as aluminum. However, the amount of electricity needed to do this on a production scale was too great for the equipment available in the early 1800s. Then the picture changed with the invention of the electric dynamo in the middle of the century. This set the stage for Hall and Heroult's success.

All during his college years, Hall experimented with ways of making aluminum. He decided that the use of electricity to change aluminum oxide into oxygen and aluminum was the simplest and cheapest approach. In the woodshed behind his house, he slowly assembled a special furnace. The day finally came when he was ready to pass electricity through the aluminum oxide. He threw the switch and waited — but nothing happened, for the aluminum oxide refused to melt. For days and days after this, he pondered on what went wrong.

At last, the thought came to him that if he started with a liquid solution containing aluminum, electric current would do the job. But first he had to find some chemical in which the oxide would dissolve. This chemical had to be a liquid as well. He read through all of the available chemistry books, but found nothing that would work. Finally he came across a mineral from Greenland called cryolite. In 1886, he melted a little cryolite, dropped aluminum oxide in and was soon beside himself with excitement. The aluminum compound did indeed dissolve in the cryolite!

With his sister's help, he prepared a clay crucible and put in cryolite and aluminum oxide. Then he inserted electrodes and passed current through the crucible's contents. But when he looked into the crucible, he found no aluminum — again something was wrong. Hall felt sure that he was on the right track. For hours

Modern aluminum production is a far cry from the woodshed laboratory of Charles Hall, the light-metal pioneer. This sketch shows a typical row of electric furnaces in which current, passed through a molten cryolite-aluminum oxide bath, frees molten aluminum to collect on the furnace bottom.

Alcoa

on end, he tried changing first one, then another part of his equipment. Finally he decided the crucible itself might be at fault. He replaced the clay crucible with a carbon one. On February 23, 1886, he tried once more.

After the melt had cooled, he broke up the material with a hammer. For the first time, embedded inside, were small masses of aluminum metal. A new industry was born.

It took years of struggle after this. Soon after Hall applied for a patent on his process, Heroult did too. This led to a long patent fight before both parties agreed to a compromise settlement. It took a lot of persuasion by Hall, Captain Alfred E. Hunt, and other pioneers to gain the financial backing needed to make large-scale aluminum production a reality. However, by the turn of the century, aluminum had been proven to be an excellent material for cooking utensils. It was a good even conductor of heat. This quality prevented the occurrence of hot spots in utensils that would cause food to burn. The first order of this type received was for 2,000 aluminum kettles. Soon after, all kinds of kitchen equipment — pots, pans, and baking dishes — were being made of aluminum. Aluminum also became important in the electrical field, since it is an excellent conductor of electricity.

In World War I, the metal's lightness led to its use in many parts of the planes that took part in the first air wars in history. Most of the aluminum in those days was used in the engines, and the rest of the plane was made of steel, wood and fabric. After World War I,

In the Hall Process of reducing aluminum from its oxide, alumina (aluminum oxide) is dissolved in a bath of molten cryolite. The process is continuous, and more alumina is added from time to time. In this photograph the potmen break the crust of alumina which forms on the surface of the bath. The plank-like members shown here are aluminum busbars through which electricity is conducted to the reduction post.

airplane designers decided that aluminum was the answer to really efficient planes that could be used in mass air travel. Aluminum's strength and lightness made it possible to carry more pounds of payload (cargo and/or passengers) until finally, airliners capable of carrying thirty, forty, and today, over 100 passengers became practical. Fighter planes and bombers of World War II were made almost exclusively of aluminum. Today, although the tremendous temperatures which some advanced missiles and aircraft generate have become too great to permit the use of pure aluminum, it still may be used in numerous ways. The tremendous Saturn booster that will power a manned flight to the moon is made almost entirely of advanced aluminum alloys.

Although the need for aluminum in military and commercial aircraft created the first great market for aluminum, aircraft manufacture now accounts for only a small part of aluminum usage. Aluminum has become a cornerstone of everyday living. It is used in building materials, in foil for kitchen use, in window

Molten aluminum is poured from the crucible into ingot molds.

Alcoa

screens, tooth paste tubes, truck bodies, canoes, freezers, air conditioners, and in thousands of other ways. Now a prime metal of today, the outlook is even brighter for tomorrow. Just one of many increasing uses for aluminum is in passenger automobiles. At present, some sixty-three pounds is used per car and there are signs that within twenty years this figure will at least triple. Lightweight gas turbine engines for super-powered cars of tomorrow are likely to be made mainly of advanced aluminum alloys. And in the world of space travel, special aluminum vehicles for moving about the surface of the moon, Mars, and other planets are already on the drawing boards.

Light metals have found many new uses in recent years. One recent example was this nearly all-aluminum Indianapolis Speedway racer built by Harvey Aluminum.

Harvey Aluminum

The other major light metal of today, magnesium, is literally "mined from the sea." Though some combinations occur widely on land, magnesium is most easy to get from the ocean. About 0.13 per cent of sea water is magnesium.

The first form of magnesium to be isolated was magnesium sulfate. This was done in 1695 by English scientist Nehemiah Grew (magnesium sulfate is the chemical name for the laxative called Epsom Salts). However, this form was often mistaken for lime, until about 1755 when Scottish chemist Joseph Black showed that the two were very different. Credit for the discovery of magnesium is usually given to Sir Humphrey Davy. In 1808, he established the fact that magnesium oxide was the oxide of a new metal. In 1828, the French chemist A. Bussy finally isolated magnesium by fusing magnesium chloride with metallic potassium. In 1833, Michael Faraday of England made larger amounts of magnesium by passing an electric current through molten magnesium chloride. German scientists later (about 1866) developed a relatively low-cost production method based on electrolysis. Germany then became the main supplier of the metal in the world until World War I. The British blockade led such firms as Dow Chemical Company in the United States to start making magnesium.

In 1941, a method was perfected to take magnesium from sea water. About eighty-five per cent of the metal used by the United States during World War II was obtained in this way. In the process, sea water is pumped into huge settling tanks and mixed with lime. Some of the elements in lime take magnesium's place in the water, and a form of the metal called magnesium hydroxide comes out of solution and settles to the tank bottom. This chemical is collected, dried, and then changed to magnesium chloride by treatment with

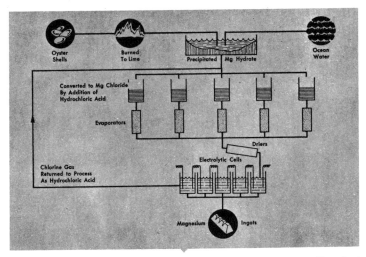

Dow Chemical

This chart shows how another light metal, magnesium, is reclaimed from sea water.

hydrochloric acid. Magnesium chloride, in turn, can be electrolyzed with electric current to separate the pure magnesium.

Magnesium is about thirty per cent lighter than aluminum. However, it is not as strong, particularly in its pure state. To get a usable material, other metals must be mixed with magnesium. These alloys of magnesium have many uses both in our country's defense and in the home. During World War II, 200 to 400 pounds of lightweight metal were used in airplane engines. Only the fact that magnesium has lower strength and poorer corrosion resistance kept it from completely replacing aluminum.

Our space vehicles such as the Vanguard satellite, the Agena booster which sent many United States space probes to the moon, sun, and Venus, and many other spacecraft are made mostly of magnesium. In recent years, more and more magnesium has been used in cars, trucks, and railroad trains, particularly in Europe. A good part of the German Volkswagen automobile is made of light magnesium alloy. Portable conveyor systems, milk crates, ladders, typewriter carriages, high-speed machine parts for textile-making equipment, vacuum cleaners, cameras, and even baseball catchers' masks are now being made of magnesium.

We find that the most widely used metals of today are iron, steel, aluminum, magnesium, and, to a lesser extent, copper, tin, and zinc. All of them will continue to play increasingly important roles in the future, and they will be joined by many other metals very soon.

4

METALS
OF TOMORROW

In the future we can expect to have submarines which will operate safely at 20,000 feet below the surface of the sea and will cruise at about 100 miles per hour, a speed three times that of the fastest atomic submarine of the 1960s.

Sounds fantastic? Perhaps, but we can expect to see them in action in a few decades.

The forerunners of such ships are already in use. Research ships such as the bathyscaph *Trieste* and *Aluminaut* can reach depths beyond the 4,000 fathom level. Of course, they can carry only two or three crew members and very little payload, but the "working" submarine of tomorrow will revolutionize water transport. Its greater efficiency will make it worthwhile to ship many cargoes where surface storms and the resistance of ocean waves will no longer be a problem.

Construction of these advanced submarines will probably require widespread use of the "metals of tomorrow," such as titanium. Steel, the metal used for the hulls of today's submarines, just isn't strong enough for the conditions met at very great depths. The tremendous pressures on a ship's hull at these levels would require having a large number of stiffeners attached to the steel skins to keep them from collapsing. The weight of the braces would make it almost impossible to carry a worthwhile amount of cargo or number of passengers. Titanium, on the other hand, is much lighter than steel, about forty-five per cent lighter. It also has much greater stiffness and would not need to be strengthened as much as steel for this use. Finally, titanium has the greatest corrosion resistance to salt water of any other metal except platinum.

Titanium is just one of a whole group of metals of tomorrow which have been studied intensively by scientists only in the past decade. Many of these metals have practical uses now, but they are likely to have major roles in the future. The amazing thing about them is the speed with which these materials have come from laboratory research to practical use.

The development of steel took hundreds of years. Aluminum took well over fifty years from early research to worthwhile use. On the other hand, titanium became a key factor in certain missile and aircraft designs just ten years after major development of the metal began. Today, it has gone beyond this. Its exceptional resistance to being eaten away by many highly corrosive chemicals makes it valuable to the chemical industry. Special tanks, valves, and pipes to contain

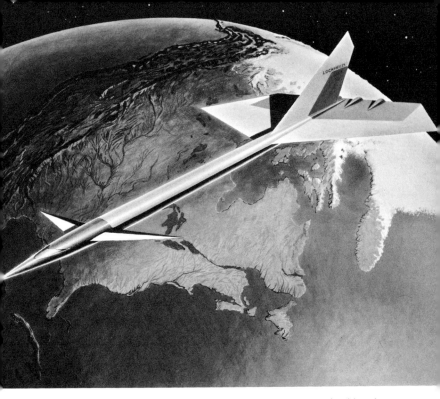

Flying at 2,200 m.p.h., a supersonic transport similar to this artist's conception could: leave London at 11 a.m. after breakfast, arrive in New York at 8:20 a.m. (another breakfast), and get to Los Angeles at 7:45 a.m. (for a third breakfast) — all in the same morning. The plane would carry 90 passengers at altitudes between 60,000 and 80,000 feet, and operate from existing airports. The Mach 3.0–3.5 transport's direct operating costs would be lower than either current subsonic jets or four-engine piston planes. It would use stainless steel and titanium in conventional construction.

hard-to-handle chemicals are now made of titanium.

Titanium was, of course, known to chemists in the laboratory long before this useful metal could be used in quantity. It was discovered in 1791 by the Reverend

William Gregor in Cornwall, England. He first called it *menaccanite*, since it was found as a part of a peculiar black mineral sand which Gregor observed at Menaccan in Cornwall.

Four years later, the German scientist M. H. Klaproth discovered a new element in a mineral called *rutile*. He called his new metal *titanium* after the Titans of Greek mythology. A few years later, he compared titanium with the element found by the Reverend Gregor and found they were the same metal. Over the years, Klaproth's name for the metal survived and the word menaccanite was forgotten. For all practical purposes, this new metal was ignored for a hundred years after its discovery. It was interesting to know that such a metal existed, but no one could see any particular use for it.

Then in the 1940s scientists began to work on many advanced materials in earnest. The growth of high-speed aircraft and missiles and the urgency provided by World War II caused researchers all over the world to study more and more materials.

Their research indicated that titanium had very impressive properties. It was strong, relatively light, and more important, could withstand temperatures of over 1,000 degrees Fahrenheit without failing. (Aluminum begins to soften and lose strength at 400 to 600 degrees Fahrenheit.) With the operating temperatures of missiles and aircraft rising steadily, it was vital to find better high-temperature materials. Soon practical ways for extracting titanium from its ores were discovered.

Ways of producing many different titanium alloys and forming them into shapes followed swiftly.

In rapid succession, many other new metals came under observation — beryllium, vanadium, columbium, tantalum, tungsten, molybdenum, chromium and, most recently, a whole group of metals (seventeen in all) called "rare earths."

Amateur geologists are all familiar with beryl. This mineral, in various forms, is the source of some of the most colorful jewels in the world. For instance, the emerald comes from a form of beryl that is bright green. (The different colors of beryl, are due to the presence of small amounts of different compounds. In emerald, the green color is due to the beryl containing a compound called chromium oxide.) Another type of beryl is yellow and from it come the gems called golden beryl. Still other forms of beryl are pink and provide jewels called morganite. Still other kinds are the sources of beautiful blue-green-colored stones called aquamarines. Finally, there is common beryl, which is white, colorless, or light green, depending on the elements that make it up.

But, in recent years, beryl has become even more valuable than ever. Not as a source of gem stones, but because another metal of tomorrow, beryllium, is extracted from it. Beryllium as an element was discovered in 1797 by L. N. Vauquelin of France and the first metallic beryllium extracted in 1828. The pure metal has a steel-gray color and is sweetish to the taste. Combined with copper, beryllium was used in many ways from the early 1900s right up to today in the electrical field. Beryllium-copper alloy springs are often used as electrical contact blades, relays, and switches.

However, only in the past several years has beryllium as a metal received concentrated attention. At first, most research was directed to uses of beryllium in atomic energy, but the greatest excitement was aroused by the metal's potential as a highly efficient structural material.

Why this very great interest? Again defense needs prompted it. Beryllium is light and strong. It is far lighter than the best aluminum alloy used today. Conventional airplanes could carry perhaps half again as much in cargo or passenger weight if beryllium were used in place of aluminum. Even more important is the ability of beryllium to withstand very high temperatures. This light metal melts at 2,360 degrees Fahrenheit. It is what is called a good heat sink or heat sponge because it can soak up large amounts of heat. Already it has proved its worth as a heat shield on the bottom of the Project Mercury capsules. It has protected astronauts from temperatures as high as 3,000 degrees during re-entry into the earth's atmosphere from space.

Scientists were faced with many difficult problems in developing beryllium as a practical material. Beryllium, true enough, had many wonderful properties, but its manufacture also presented many possible roadblocks. Perhaps the most dangerous property of the metal is that in certain forms it can be a killer. Beryllium in its final, solid shape is perfectly safe. It can be touched or handled just as a piece of aluminum or steel is handled without danger to the handler. But when beryllium is heated beyond a certain point so that its surfaces turn to vapor, or if surface pieces come off in the form of very fine dust, inhaling it can make a person very ill and even cause death.

The only time this characteristic could be hazardous was when the beryllium was being machined on a lathe or put through some of the other processes used when making parts from it. Scientists made tests, then found special ways of handling the metal. In a beryllium manufacturing plant all the machines have large suction devices installed around and above them which draw off all dust, chips, and vapor created when the metal is cut or formed. Other special precautions include careful control of the factory air and protective clothing for workmen. As a result, beryllium poisoning has been made a thing of the past.

When danger from the poisonous metal was eliminated, scientists struggled to improve the material itself. Beryllium is not as brittle as glass, yet a sudden blow could cause a sheet of the metal to break or crack. The same blow on a ductile metal, such as aluminum or stainless steel, would cause it, at the most, to buckle or bend slightly. Obviously, before beryllium could be used in large sections for such things as vehicle skins or fittings, this problem had to be solved.

Scientists all over the world began looking at everything concerned with beryllium, right down to the metal's atomic structure. They examined some samples under very high powered microscopes and subjected other samples to all kinds of tests. These ranged from pulling samples apart in tension machines to seeing how specimens withstood high temperatures in special furnaces.

They decided that one way to get more ductile beryllium was to make the metal as close to 100 per cent pure as possible. Special production processes were developed after many months and years of testing to remove all foreign elements. These impurities might consist of traces of iron or aluminum so slight they amounted to less than one part in a million parts of beryllium.

Then they also studied the way beryllium crystals developed as the metal was treated. Depending on how a material is produced from its raw state, the internal structure can be made of large crystals of the metal or smaller ones. It was found that the smaller the beryllium crystals could be made, the more ductile the final product. Both these approaches have been applied at the same times. Slowly, as scientists made very pure beryllium with finer crystals, the ductility was improved.

Today, beryllium is still a brittle material, but it is far less brittle than just two or three years ago. It has been given bending ability so that, by careful design, useful beryllium structures can be made. Using special methods, men can make beryllium channels over twenty-four feet long. Thin sheets of the metal suitable for skins are being made in sections three feet wide by eight feet long. The sections begin as a very fine powder of beryllium. The powder is then squeezed into a solid sheet under high temperatures and pressures. Already sample sections of beryllium skin are undergoing tests and all signs point to widespread use of it in the fuselages of the manned spaceships of tomorrow.

For spaceships, beryllium has a particularly useful quality. It forms an excellent meteoroid bumper. The many small pieces of meteors found in space can be a hazard. If a tiny particle should puncture a space ship's skin, the ship's air supply could rush out, resulting in death for the passengers. Beryllium is one of several materials that have great resistance to penetration by fast-moving particles such as these.

In the future, beryllium will become a key missile-space metal. But its many outstanding properties indicate that it will have many other uses in more "down to earth" fields. Already beryllium "windows" are important parts of X-ray machines. In such machines, the X-rays must be restricted so that they go out only in certain desired directions. The portions of X-rays wanted for taking X-ray pictures of parts of the body pass quite easily through beryllium. On the other hand, more harmful radiation is absorbed by the metal. In instruments, electrical devices, and gyroscopes, beryllium's lightness and good electrical properties also make it a very promising metal of the future.

67

Extremes of temperature create continual problems in many areas of advanced science. The propellants that power many types of missile engines are stored at temperatures hundreds of degrees below zero. Liquid hyrogen must be held at minus 423 degrees Fahrenheit and liquid oxygen is stored at minus 320 degrees. Once a rocket is in operation parts of the engine must withstand temperatures of thousands of degrees. Later in the mission, when the payload — either a nose cone or a manned re-entry craft — comes back into the atmosphere, wing and fuselage leading edges must withstand heat that turns them a glowing red. Some materials must withstand only the extremes of cold. Others are needed to take the almost unbelievable heat. And some must be able to do both without losing strength.

To find answers to many of these problems, scientists turned their attention to a group of materials called *refractory metals* because they have extremely high melting points. The metals studied most carefully in this work are: molybdenum, columbium, tantalum, tungsten, vanadium, and chromium. Work on vanadium and chromium is in its very early stages. Chromium, of course, is familiar, since thin films of it are plated onto steel to provide the chrome finishes for automobile bumpers and trim. Now scientists are making sheets and structural shapes of chromium metal in hopes of taking advantage of the metal's high melting point of 3,405 degrees Fahrenheit.

However, most research up to now has concentrated

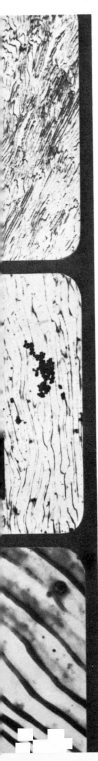

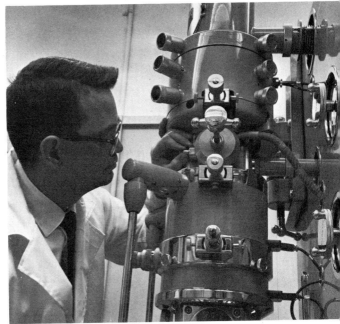

Rocketdyne

Ally of scientist in finding out the secrets of materials structure is the electron beam microscope. Shown here is one used which can magnify a material sample 250,000 times. Making enlargements from small areas of pictures taken, a high magnification can increase this value to 2½ million times. At the left are successively greater magnifications of a sample of one of the "metals of tomorrow," columbium. Top picture is magnified 1,000 times normal size, middle one is 8,000 times, and bottom one, 24,000 times.

on the first four refractory metals. Tungsten has the highest melting point of any metallic element. It will take temperatures of over 6,100 degrees before becoming molten, although it loses much strength at temperatures lower than this. Tantalum has a melting point of 5,425 degrees Fahrenheit. Molybdenum and columbium melt at 4,730 and 4,380 degrees respectively.

An example of a material which can perform well over a wide range of temperatures is tantalum alloyed with columbium. This alloy is useful from minus 400 degrees to 3,000 degrees.

Several alloys with tantalum as the base and columbium as the main alloying element are useful over great temperature ranges. One of these was made of sixty-five per cent tantalum, thirty per cent columbium, and five per cent vanadium. Another had the same amount of columbium, but a little less tantalum and a little more, seven and one-half per cent, vanadium. A third had sixty per cent tantalum, thirty per cent columbium, and ten per cent vanadium.

It is not so surprising that tantalum and columbium should work so well together. In nature, tantalum is always found in combination with columbium. Columbium, which is a silver-white metal, was named by Charles Hatchett who first extracted a compound of it in 1801. Tantalum was found and named the following year by A. G. Ekeberg. However, the fact that the two metals were always found together caused much confusion among researchers, confusion that was not completely cleared up until 1866 when J. C. G. de Marignac of France found a way to separate the two.

Tantalum, which resembles but is somewhat darker than platinum, found favor for special uses long before columbium. The metal has outstanding resistance to corrosive chemicals and most acids. For this reason, by the mid-1920s, a relatively large amount of tantalum sheet was being produced for use in chemical plants. Typical applications included devices known as heat exchangers, evaporators, condensers, and acid absorbers. More recently, doctors found that tantalum could be used in the human body with little effect on tissues. Some metals, for instance, could cause harmful irritation or might react with tissues to cause infection. Tantalum wire and thin plates of the metal are now widely used by surgeons in nerve and bone operations to hold tissues together or cover bone removal areas. In electronics, tantalum's good electrical resistance properties have quite recently led to its widespread use in devices called capacitors. In the circuits of the average radio and television sets there are many small, cylindrical devices. Many of these are capacitors.

Columbium was for a long time regarded by metal producers only as an annoyance. It hindered their production of useful tantalum. In recent years, though, science has shown that columbium also has many very promising capabilities for future uses. These range from high-temperature engine and spacecraft structure to use in atomic power facilities.

Redoubled efforts have been made to develop columbium alloys, and large plants to produce the metal have been built. Though work is scarcely under way, indications are that columbium will actually be used in much greater volume than tantalum in the future. The main reason for this is that the metal has good strength and other properties in line with those of tantalum at extreme temperatures, but it is quite a bit lighter. This means that columbium could be extremely useful in spacecraft construction where it is always important to have maximum strength and light weight.

Molybdenum is an element that was known before the birth of Christ. It was discussed by Aristotle more than 2,000 years ago. However, there was often much confusion about it, for the mineral containing molybdenum was difficult to tell from several other minerals. In early writings, the terms molybdena, plumbago, graphite, and galna were often mixed up. Sometimes the author was referring to molybdenum, but sometimes he really meant graphite. Finally, in 1778, Swedish chemist Karl Wilhelm Scheele showed how to tell which ores contained molybdenum, and in 1782, P. J. Helm separated out the pure metal. Today, molybdenum is produced as a finely divided gray powder.

The source of ninety per cent of the world's molybdenum is in the United States at the Americal Climax mine in Climax, Colorado. It has been used for many years as an alloying element in steel. A small amount has greatly improved the properties of steel. Molybdenum is used by itself for plates, grids, and support wires in vacuum tubes for radio, television, and other purposes. Recently, sheet molybdenum has helped solve high temperature rocket problems. The flame skirt around the exhaust nozzle of the Rocketdyne 1,500,000-pound-thrust rocket engine is made of molybdenum.

Scheele, the man who did so much work on molybdenum, was also the first to recognize tungsten in 1781. The word tungsten means heavy stone, and the metal was so named because it is very dense and heavy. This metal is outstanding in an amazing number of ways. It has the highest melting point of any metal, the highest tensile strength, it can produce the highest musical note, it can be drawn into the finest wire, and it has the lowest expansion rate. Tungsten's melting point is so high that it can't be cast into rods the usual way. With most metals, the metal is melted in a crucible and then poured into a rod mold. But tungsten is molten at so high a temperature that every crucible material, including graphite, would melt first. To obtain cast parts, tungsten powder is put in special molds and great pressure applied. The pressure causes a release of internal energy in the metal so that the particles fuse into the desired shape.

Most of us are familiar with the use of tungsten filaments in electric light bulbs. Tungsten also has been widely used in other areas in electricity such as in electrical contacts and as a protective sheet in radium beam therapy. Small amounts of tungsten also provide better steel for armor plate and for automobile bodies.

However, all of these uses require only a very small amount of the metal.

Now scientists are considering sheet tungsten for many high temperature uses. Tungsten jetavators are presently used to steer rockets. The jetavators are vanes placed in the exhaust flow from a rocket engine. By changing the vane's position, the hot gas is deflected one way or the other, causing the rocket to change course. Tungsten is just about the only metal that can withstand the temperatures in a rocket's exhaust blast without melting away. The heat of a rocket blast reaches more than 4,000 degrees. More and more tungsten will be used in spacecraft and in civilian high temperature applications as we increase our knowledge of this metal of tomorrow.

To move on to even more exotic sounding metals, let's examine the rare earths. Paradoxically, they are not rare. As scientist E. V. Kleber notes, they are half as abundant as carbon and chlorine and even the scarcest are more abundant than cadmium, silver, bismuth, gold or platinum.

Apart from scandium and yttrium, the rare earths in order of increasing atomic number are: lanthanum, cerium, praesodymium, neodymium, promethium, samarium, europium, gadolinium, terbium, dysprosium, holmium, erbium, thulium, ytterbium and lutetium. (Of the above, one does not occur naturally. This is promethium, which is one of the materials produced after atomic fission.)

The existence of rare earths and the general outline

of their atomic properties have been known for some time. But very little was known in detail about each of these metals until recently. Chemically, they all are very much alike and thus a great many of them are usually found together. Their chemical similarity has made them extremely difficult to separate from one another. In fact, while the other metals we've discussed were separated out in the late 1700s or early 1800s, it has only been in the past few years that methods were perfected to get pure samples of each of the rare earths. As a result, it is only now that scientists are able to begin tests on each metal to find out its properties. Chemically the metals are alike. In their physical properties — that is their strength, magnetic and electrical properties, and melting points — they are quite different.

Already there are indications that these seventeen metals will be used widely in many fields. By adding a little cerium to oil used in jet engines, the temperature limit of the oil has been raised from 400 up to 575 degrees. Some of the metals have some properties similar to conventional "light" alloys. Scandium, for instance, has some resemblance to aluminum and yttrium to titanium. In some cases, the rare earths seem to have better properties than some light alloys. Some of them can withstand chemicals and gases that would attack conventional light alloys. This might well herald major structural uses for some rare earths.

Still other rare earths have very promising magnetic properties. These include gadolinium, terbium, dysprosium, holmium and erbium. This could lead to development of magnets with many new properties and uses. For instance, very strong magnets might be developed in place of latches to hold large building doors closed. More important, magnets are used in many ways in advanced electronic devices, from computers to communication systems, and new types of magnets could vastly improve some of these devices.

Rare earths seem promising as *semiconductors*. This is the amazing new breed of electronic materials that led to development of the transistor. The transistor and other devices like it replaced bulky radio and television tubes and made possible the construction of the miniature sets of today. Even more astounding advances in semiconducting materials are in the laboratory stage. Someday it may be possible to compress radios to wristwatch size or smaller and make computers that will fit into the palm of your hand. The rare earth materials lanthanum, neodymium, and dysprosium are being tested as semiconductors for such uses. In the nuclear area too, such rare earths as samarium, europium, and gadolinium have properties unmatched by any other metals for certain uses.

The fact that there has been great interest in rare earths is dramatically illustrated by the rapidly decreasing prices of such materials. Increased use has brought about greater production and, therefore, lower prices. In 1959 and 1960, neodymium compounds cost $30 to $40 for a half gram (equivalent to $20,000 to $30,000 per pound). Today 100 grams costs six or seven dollars, or less than $300 per pound.

This then has been a quick glance at the metals of the future. Their names may be strange right now. But only a short time ago, the metal aluminum was considered an exotic, rarely encountered material by the man in the street. Today, refrigerators all over the United States are stocked with foods protected by aluminum foil. Aluminum cooking utensils, awnings, siding, and automobile bodies are just a few of hundreds of other everyday uses for this commonplace metal.

In years to come, many of the metals just discussed will find their way into radios, television sets, transportation vehicles, and yet undreamed of applications. Keep your eye on the metals of tomorrow.

5

THE NEW
CERAMICS

SCENE: *almost 10,000 years ago.* In a small clearing in the middle of an almost impenetrable forest a man sits in front of a rude mud hut. He takes a lump of spongy material in his hands and puts it into a bowl-shaped apparatus. He spins the apparatus with his feet. As the bowl spins, he works the spongy material with his hands until it takes the shape of the bowl.

SCENE: *today.* High above the atmosphere, the nose cone of a missile arcs back down toward earth. As it enters the atmosphere, friction heat causes temperatures of thousands of degrees to play on the shiny white surface of the cone. Despite this, the cone comes through safely carrying another set of important instrument readings from outer space.

What have these two happenings in common? Simply that both the material being shaped in the ancient potter's wheel and the heat-resisting nose cone are made of ceramic. In all likelihood, both are made of the same ceramic — aluminum oxide — obtained from a form of clay.

Aluminum oxide is a mineral made of aluminum combined with oxygen. As we saw in the last chapter, the metal aluminum is obtained from aluminum oxide. Yet though this is one of the most widely used ceramic materials, it is also, paradoxically, an exception. The reason is that the term ceramic, in its strict definition, refers to products made of nonmetallic materials. The National Institute of Ceramic Engineers once defined ceramics as those products "which are composed of inorganic, nonmetallic mineral materials, prepared and fabricated in any of a variety of methods and usually subjected to high temperatures during manufacture." Examples of ceramic materials that contain no metallic elements are lime, a compound of calcium and oxygen; silica, a combination of silicon and oxygen; and boron nitride, a compound of boron and nitrogen.

Still, many materials called ceramics are made up of metals combined with some other nonmetallic element, such as oxygen, sulphur, nitrogen, or carbon. Another way to separate ceramics from other types of materials is to consider that most ceramics originally are found in the form of clay. Clay is any soft, earthy material which becomes plastic and sticky when wet.

Usually we think of ceramics as dishes, vases, or ashtrays, but the term includes much more. Just about all building and paving bricks, cement, lime, and plaster are ceramic products. Other ceramic items include glass, enamel, glazes, abrasives, acid-proof ware, thermal insulating products, electrical insulating materials, and electrical porcelain. You see ceramic coatings in the form of enamels or glazes everywhere you

Anchor Metals

Ceramics are widely used as electrical insulators. A typical case is in these high-power electrical towers. The series of top-like devices from which the electrical wires hang are ceramic insulators.

go. The shiny surfaces of stoves, washing machines, sinks, and bathtubs are just a few examples.

Ceramics are one of the most ancient materials, but in another sense they are one of the most modern. Some of the most amazing scientific advances of today and tomorrow depend on what might be called new ceramic technology. An example is in the field of electronics, where many vital parts are made wholly or partly of ceramic materials. A modern automobile engine would not run without the ceramic-coated spark plugs that ignite the fuel mixture in the cylinders.

Interest in ceramics continues to increase because, in general, they have many properties not found in other materials. They are best known for their resistance to heat. Among metals, only tungsten can take very extreme temperatures, but even it melts at 6,100 degrees Fahrenheit. On the other hand, there are a number of ceramics which can withstand this much heat and more. Zirconium carbide maintains its qualities at temperatures over 6,150 degrees and tantalum carbide can resist heat of more than 7,000 degrees. Ordinary carbon — which we see as such things as pencil lead or soot — in certain forms, such as graphite or pyrographite, can take up to 6,600 degrees.

Aside from such metals as tungsten, tantalum, columbium, and molybdenum, most metals melt at much lower temperatures. The strongest steel alloys become soft at temperatures above 1,500 to 2,000 degrees Fahrenheit. Even superalloys, such as cobalt-base and nickel-base materials, have little strength above 2,200 degrees. Aluminum oxide, on the other hand, doesn't decompose until 3,960 degrees Fahrenheit. There are literally dozens of other ceramics that can withstand temperatures of over 3,000 degrees with ease. To name just a few, silicon carbide, 4,200; boron nitride, 5,280; boron carbide, 4,400; zircon 4,520; and silica, 3,130.

Still another property of ceramics is the ability to withstand attacks by acids and other corrosive compounds. Everyone is aware that an iron surface exposed to air soon becomes covered with rust. Aluminum also takes on a spotty, dull look when it stays in the open air. This is caused by the reaction of the metal with some of the elements in the air such as oxygen. The oxygen combines with some of the metal to form what often is a weaker material. In other words, the oxygen corrodes or eats away the metal. On some metals this is a good thing. A protective oxide coating forms and prevents further corrosion. Such a coating is really a thin, corrosion-resistant film of ceramic.

Elements such as hydrogen, as well as some of the things contained in sea water, and strong acids also dramatically affect certain metals and plastics. Sea water will completely corrode an uncoated sheet of magnesium in a matter of days.

But many ceramics will easily take long exposure to some of these corrosive elements without the least bit of damage. Of course, this does not mean that each ceramic will withstand all kinds of damaging environments. The designer has to choose the right ceramic for a given job. Graphite can endure very high temperatures and will not be too much affected by oxygen in the air, but at high temperatures it is very sensitive to hydrogen and can be readily eroded away if not protected by some special coating.

Ceramics also have many properties of great importance to electronic and electrical systems. In particular, most ceramics are good insulators. An insulator is a material that does not readily conduct an electric current. You might compare an electric current to the flow of water in a pipe. To have water come out a faucet, you must guide it from the water main to the faucet without have the water leak away into the earth.

In the same way, an electric current must flow in certain directions without leaking away. You can't surround electric wire with metal pipe because most metals are good conductors of electricity; in fact, this is why copper or aluminum wire is used to carry current from one place to another. If you tried to surround a wire with another metal, the current would flow right through the metal and into the ground. Instead, a container or pipe must be made of a non-conducting material, which might be rubber, certain plastics, or ceramics. Ceramics are usually too brittle to be used as covers on metal electrical wire, even though they may have better insulating properties than rubber and some plastics.

However, there are many areas where the ability to bend isn't required and here ceramics do play key parts. An example is on high power lines where electric lines are supported by poles or where the lines feed into certain kinds of joints. If you look at electric lines feeding into homes or factories, you can see many top-shaped, white or colored parts a few inches high on which the wires are supported. These are made of ceramic and insulate the wire from the poles or other areas to which the wires are attached. As has been mentioned earlier, automobile spark plugs are insulated with ceramic jackets. In the field of electronics, ceramics, in the form of thin coatings or small parts, play important roles as insulators.

In the electrical field of tomorrow, ceramics may play an even greater role. In fact, scientists at Westinghouse Electric recently pointed out that ceramics, rather than iron and steel, may be the critical materials for building the electric power generators of tomorrow. These generators would provide the current to heat homes and office buildings, provide electricity for lighting, and do all the other things conventional steel, copper, and iron generators of today do. There would be one major difference. The generators of tomorrow would provide fantastically greater amounts of current with little or no increase in cost or size over today's electric equipment.

These generators of tomorrow are called magnetohydrodynamic (or MHD) generators. In them, a stream of ionized conducting gas called a plasma replaces the moving copper conductors of a conventional generator. (Look into a small electric motor and you will see that the revolving part has a series of copper windings. A generator in a large power plant has the same sort of arrangement, only on a much bigger scale.) The plasma moves at speeds up to 2,000 miles per hour at temperatures of 5,000 degrees Fahrenheit. If a modern automobile were placed in this plasma stream, it would soon become a big puddle of melted material.

The problem in building MHD generators is to find a material able to contain the hot, ionized gas under these conditions. (By an ionized gas, we mean one whose atoms have been slightly altered so they form conductors of electricity.) Westinghouse Electric ran tests on hundreds of materials and finally found that only certain kinds of ceramics would work. The two best ceramics were magnesium oxide and zirconium oxide.

Without ceramics, many major materials could not be made. The outer shells of furnaces used in making iron and steel are made of high-strength steel, but the tremendous temperatures of the flames inside would easily melt the shells if the furnace interior were not lined with blocks of heat-resistant ceramics.

The ceramics industry is constantly turning out furnace blocks to take higher and higher temperatures for longer times. For many years, a ceramic called silicon carbide was used for such parts. In the past few years, a new silicon carbide material in which the silicon carbide grains are held together with another silicon compound called silicon nitride was introduced.

The new ceramic actually increases in strength with increasing temperature up to about 1,832 degrees Fahrenheit. The new material is twice as strong at 2,450 degrees Fahrenheit as the older type.

Of course, ceramic linings are widely used in many other industries besides metal-making. The glass which forms our home and automobile windows, fluorescent light tubes, and pickle jars originates in tanks of molten glass where temperatures are over 3,000 degrees. Certain specialty glass containers, such as the white opaque jars used for cold cream, extremely corrosive lead glass, borosilicate glass used in certain types of lamps, television set face plates, and coffee pots pose added problems. Glass for these purposes must be made at high temperatures and mixed with very corrosive acids. Only special kinds of ceramic linings can hold such materials during their manufacture. There are four types of ceramics from which these linings usually are made. These include two kinds of aluminum oxide(the difference between the two is based on their having different crystal structures): aluminum oxide saturated with chromium, and zirconia-aluminum oxide.

Electronics is another area in which advanced ceramics may be responsible for major breakthroughs. Most of today's electronic devices, from television sets to complex space communication equipment, depend on the use of parts made of materials known as semiconductors. Semiconductors are certain kinds of solid materials which can conduct electric current in the same way that a radio tube does, but they are used in devices much smaller than tubes. Probably the best known semiconductor is the transistor. Most transistors are made of silicon and germanium. Silicon and germanium are not ceramic materials. Although transistors resist heat better than vacuum tubes, they too stop functioning properly at temperatures above 300 degrees.

In many new projects being studied by scientists, electronic devices must work at temperatures well over 1,000 degrees. An example of this is the rocket engine controls of a spaceship or certain electronic systems for use with advanced nuclear reactors.

We've seen that most ceramics are very good insulators — that is, they prevent electric current from flowing through them. But among the hundreds of different ceramics known today, there are a few that have opposite properties. With their high temperature strength, these conducting ceramics might make possible the development of very high-temperature electronic equipment. The most likely material for this purpose is silicon carbide which can perform electronic tasks at temperatures of 1,800 degrees Fahrenheit. A special type of silicon carbide called single-crystal is needed. As a very high-powered microscope would show, ordinary silicon carbide is made up of many small crystals. Just as the phrase indicates, single-crystal silicon carbide is composed of just one big crystal. Scientists are working to develop special furnaces and silicon carbide forming methods to produce the required type of ceramic.

Thus far we've talked about the amazingly good properties of ceramics. Unfortunately, ceramics are brittle, and this characteristic limits their use. An obvious example is ceramic pottery. If a fine piece of china or even heavy ceramic ware is dropped on the floor, it probably will shatter into many pieces. While there are stronger ceramic materials, generally it is true of all ceramics that they are brittle.

If ceramics could be bent into various shapes, it would be a major revolution even in today's advanced materials technology. For instance, most electrical wire today is covered with an insulating jacket of rubber or plastic. In many cases, a thin ceramic coating could provide better insulation and the wire could be much thinner and lighter. Such a coating can be placed on the wire today, but the moment the wire bends, the coating "crazes." That is, it develops many fine cracks ruining the insulation, or it may flake off the wire altogether.

After World War II, many scientists started to search for a ductile ceramic. (Ductile means the ability to be bent.) One of the first ideas was to try to find some combined material having the good properties of both metals and ceramics. By putting together a metal and a ceramic, it was reasoned, this might be done. Experiments resulted in a new kind of material called a cermet. For instance, aluminum oxide might be used as a cermet base and to it a certain percentage of chromium might be mixed in. Another example of a promising cermet is titanium carbide particles bonded together with nickel.

Many of these looked interesting. Titanium carbide and aluminum oxide base cermets were developed that could be made into blades for high-temperature aircraft gas turbine engines. Some test engines were made and these ran well for a while. But engines often suck in stray particles, such as bolts, gravel, etc., and sooner or later these would strike a ceramic blade in just the right way to break it. Now this happens to metal turbine blades too, but here one broken blade won't keep the engine from running, for the other blades are ductile enough to bend a bit without breaking if struck. In the case of the cermets, the minute one snapped, it hit against the other blades, eventually breaking all of them. In other areas as well, it was found that cermets still were closer to ceramics than metals in brittleness. After a number of years of effort, scientists reluctantly decided that cermets were not the answer to ductile ceramics.

This doesn't mean that all this work was wasted. In themselves, cermets provided new materials that could be used where brittleness wasn't so much of a problem. For instance, such cermets as bonded titanium carbide could be used in tips of very strong new cutting tools for machining new steels and other metal alloys. Without these cermet tools, much of the recently developed high-strength, high-temperature steel and some of the exotic metals discussed in chapter four would be almost impossible to machine cut. Many rotating machines depend on the use of ball-bearing joints. Usually these balls are made of metal, but in recent years many new machines and devices rotate faster and faster, raising the friction temperatures the bearings must withstand. Where these temperatures have exceeded the limits of metals, cermet bearings have come into use.

Besides trying to develop cermets, scientists naturally tried new ceramic combinations. None seemed to overcome the brittleness problem to any extent. Finally, it was decided to go back to basics. Instead of trying out many combinations, scientists began examining the atomic structure of ceramics. They wanted to find out how the atoms and molecules go together to make what we know as a ceramic. One result was the realization that impurities played a great part in determining properties of ceramics. In a given ceramic there were frequently traces of elements other than the main ones. In aluminum oxide, for instance, there might be an atom or two of chromium or iron mixed into perhaps several hundred times this number of aluminum and oxygen atoms. Scientists reasoned that these impurities might cause flaws in the material that caused it to fracture. But this wasn't the only thing they found. It was also discovered that many ceramics had a very porous structure. Even if it wasn't possible to make the material easier to bend, they thought, it might be possible to make ceramics much stronger by eliminating microscopic air holes.

Scientists at Battelle Memorial Institute, Columbus,

Ohio, point out that their studies show ceramics theoretically have strength in the range of millions of pounds per square inch. Until recently, the strength of most ceramics was measured only in thousands. What this means can be seen by comparing the figure with the strength of steel. The strongest steel alloy can take a load of three to four hundred thousand pounds on every square inch of surface without failing. When it does fail, it tends to stretch out of shape. Ceramics have potentially three or more times the strength of steel. Of course, if such a strong ceramic were overloaded, it would fail in a different way from steel. The ceramic would simply crack and fall apart instantly.

Much progress has already been made in improving ceramic strength by removing both impurities and pinholes. Carefully purified starting materials are used to make these new ceramics. Then special production methods are used in which great pressure is applied to the starting materials under high temperatures. Work is done in a carefully controlled atmosphere to keep out impurities which could get into the ceramic. The combination of pure materials, careful pressure, and temperature control makes possible elimination of airholes and results in production of high-density ceramic. The strength of some ceramics, particularly beryllium oxide and the widely known aluminum oxide, has been doubled and tripled.

What does this mean in a practical sense? While a ceramic still can't be bent very much, it can withstand much more outside force without breaking. One of the new ceramic cooking utensils sold under the trade name Pyroceram® can be dropped on the floor or even from a second-story window and it will not break. On the other hand, if it were dropped from the top of a ten-story building, it would not only break but shatter into small pieces. By comparison, a steel part might be dented after such a fall, but it would still be usable.

Increased strength in ceramics, even without ductility, has made it possible to do new things with these materials. The Pyroceram material, developed by Corning Glass, is made of a glass-aluminum oxide ceramic. Because it is an excellent heat conductor, Pyroceram is used to make extreme-temperature food containers. These can be stored in a freezer, taken out and heated on a stove, and later put back in the freezer, without any damage to the container.

In the meantime, scientists continue the struggle to find a truly bendable ceramic. For many years, most of the materials experts felt this task was hopeless. The few scientists who felt there was some possibility labored long hours in their laboratories. Stronger microscopes were brought into use, including the electron microscopes which can magnify pictures of material structures by as much as two to three hundred thousand times. Detailed mathematical theories were worked out on the energy involved in the atomic structure of ceramic material. As they found out more and more about how the ceramic atoms went together, scientists began trying to build new ceramics with better properties.

In the many studies, a large number of various types of ceramics have been tested, with emphasis on complete elimination of undesirable impurities and very close control of the crystal structure. Despite this, ductile ceramics seem a long way in the future. There is even an argument about whether such a ceramic is even remotely practical to produce on a useful scale. Some researchers say that the best that can be hoped for is a continued increase in ceramic strength. Others maintain that there is really nothing that has been seen so far in the atomic structure of ceramics that would indicate ductility is impossible to achieve.

The optimists do have something to point to in recent years that gives a glimmer of hope. An exciting report came from the laboratories of the National Aeronautics and Space Administration in 1960. Scientists at this federal research agency succeeded in making a small piece of a ceramic — magnesium oxide — in the form of a single crystal. They had bent the material almost double and it did not crack! This proved indeed that ductility could be imparted to a ceramic. However, the sample was only about an inch square. To make any larger piece of the material with a structure having only one crystal was not possible then and is not possible now. However, scientists now have a lead. They have gone back to work to try to find basic multi-crystalline structures of magnesium oxide that will have at least some of the bendability of the one-crystal samples.

Success is not assured, but if the secret of ductile

ceramics ever is found, it will be an advance for mankind comparable to the discovery of iron. Most of the problems involving materials to withstand high temperatures in space and high-speed air travel would be solved if ductile ceramics were available. Vehicles made of ductile ceramics could easily go through the so-called heat barrier without even the slightest damage to either sensitive instruments or to passengers. From a more down-to-earth standpoint, a man could put on a lightweight coverall made with a thin ceramic coating and walk right through a blazing building or a blast furnace without even feeling warm. Flexible insulation would vastly improve everyday life by making close-to-perfect heat control of buildings, automobiles, and every other type of enclosure possible. Many other developments which we can't foresee would come into being with such materials available.

The search for a ductile ceramic is expensive both in time and money but it's a scientific fight well worth the cost.

6

PLASTICS: TODAY'S WONDER MATERIALS

Dacron, Nylon, Formica, and Vinyl are all trade names which have become a part of our language. These names and hundreds of others less familiar refer to those versatile materials known as plastics.

Plastics are perhaps the greatest contribution of the modern chemical industry. They are used in making toys, stockings, dishes, automobile bodies, adhesives, and missile parts, to name only a few of the varied ways in which plastics have found their place in our daily lives.

This new industry was born as a result of developments in the ancient science of chemistry. For most of its history, the chemical industry has been traditionally the source of substances used in manufacturing other materials. In early America a typical chemical plant might produce alum for tanning hides, acid for use in making textiles, and potash for soap and glass.

In 1908 Dr. Leo Baekeland made a discovery which

changed this approach to chemical production. For the first time, chemical plants would manufacture a material which was ready to be molded, cut, or stamped into a finished item. Dr. Baekeland found a new kind of material with vastly different properties from other chemicals. This material was called Bakelite after its discoverer. Of course, it was a long way from the laboratory experiment of 1908 to a practical, useful material. It took a lot of study before scientists figured out how to make large batches of plastic that would hold together properly.

As Dr. Guy Suits, Vice President of Research and Development at General Electric noted, "Most anything you could make from those early plastics would fall apart in your hands and, if you wanted to make something really strong, you had to use a metal or alloy." As Dr. Suits reports, probably the first major items made from plastic were toothbrush handles. (Today's toothbrush, from handle to bristles, is made entirely of plastic.) For a long time, most people thought plastics were useful only for toothbrush handles.

To make plastic the wonder material it is today, scientists had to delve down to the atomic level and try to find out what makes a plastic. The structure of metal, they knew, was made up of a great many tiny crystals of the metal bonded together. In each individual crystal, scientists found that the atoms were lined up in an orderly way, one on top of or alongside another in more or less straight rows. A plastic was found to be made up of chains of atoms that twisted

These pictures show the difference in general structure between metals and plastics. The top photographs show the way a metal is made of millions of crystals which, in turn, are each made up of rows of atoms. The spaghetti-like nature of plastics is shown in the lower left. The white lines in the picture at lower right stand for chemical "bonds" which tie "spaghetti" together to give stronger plastics.

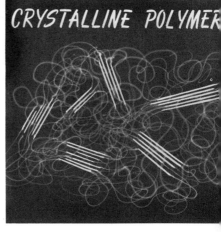

CRYSTALLINE POLYMER

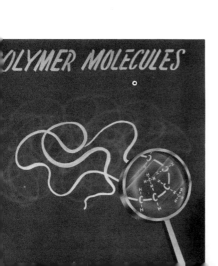

OLYMER MOLECULES

off in every direction, like the contents of a bowl of spaghetti. If one of the plastic "spaghetti" strands was pushed, it moved around easily since it didn't push up against a row of other plastic molecules, in the way that a similar row of metal molecules might do.

The term scientists use in referring to plastics is the word "polymer." This is taken from the Greek words poly, meaning many, and mers, meaning units. It refers to the property that makes a plastic so different in the way it acts from a metal or ceramic. A polymer molecule is made up of extremely large chains of smaller units. These units in turn are composed of such familiar elements as carbon, nitrogen, and hydrogen joined together. The units join together to make the polymer molecule vastly larger than the molecules making up other kinds of materials, even though the ingredients of both might be the same general types of elements. A polymer molecule might contain from 1,000 to over 200,000 atoms. By contrast, a common gas might contain only sixteen or twenty atoms in each molecule.

As David Lyman of Stanford Research Institute, Palo Alto, California, points out, "the very large size of polymer molecules bestows on them properties of strength, toughness, elasticity, and high viscosity." Viscosity refers to a sluggishness in movement. If a polymer compound and non-polymer compound, both in the liquid state, are poured down two side-by-side channels, the non-plastic probably will flow as freely as water. The plastic will be thick and will flow about the way cold molasses does. The reason, says Lyman, is that the long, flexible polymer molecules are entangled and thus prevent the solution from moving rapidly.

In their quest for stronger plastics, the first answer scientists came up with was to put in certain kinds of chemicals which, in effect, tie the polymer strands together. They call this approach cross-linking. This method helped pave the way for the first step forward. Now plastics could be made that wouldn't "fall apart in your hands." Soon small molded buttons, toys, and other compact items began to be turned out in factories throughout the United States. The strength increase, though, was not enough to let engineers use plastics in places where heavy loads had to be taken.

On the other hand, improvements could be made on cross-linking to make possible new plastics strong enough for a great many everyday jobs. One of the first of these was synthetic fiber like Nylon which was announced by Du Pont in 1938. Within a few years after Nylon was introduced, plastic stockings were worn by women throughout the world, just about eliminating the silk stockings that were used before. As time went on, more and more plastic fibers appeared, making possible plastic clothing of all types from suits to sweaters. Many of these fibers or special plastic coatings led to great advances in clothing, including almost completely waterproof garments. A more recent development was dresses and shirts that could be cleaned in a home washing machine without the garments losing shape.

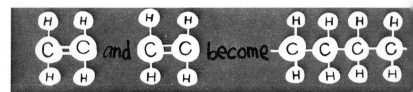

Addition Polymerization

Stanford Research Institute

Sketches show how two kinds of plastic chains are made. The top sketch shows how two similar molecules are added to form one longer plastic chain. Condensation polymers at bottom are made of two somewhat different materials which react together to form a plastic, and another material (water), which is taken away to leave the plastic. An example of a condensation polymer is Nylon.

Condensation Polymerization

Tying the various plastic strands together helped improve the strength of the material, but scientists found that still stronger plastics could be made by straightening out the "spaghetti" and lining it up. Doing this took a lot of complex testing and development of special machines, but year by year, better and better "ordering" of the plastic material took place. As a result, many fairly strong plastics are being used today in places where metal once was the only material that could be used. In addition, plastic is much lighter than metal, so it was possible to save weight in many cases.

A prime example of this weight saving is the "filament wound rocket case." For many years, the containers used to hold solid rocket propellants were made of metal. The trouble was that very high-strength, relatively heavy metals had to be used. These metals, usually some kind of special steel, were also very hard to form to the needed shape. The resulting rocket was strong enough, but a great amount of the rocket was dead weight. That is, the rocket case didn't contribute to rocket power, all it did was hold the propellant.

Then research engineers decided that one approach to cutting down dead weight in rocket cases might be to use some form of plastic. It had to be both extremely strong and also easy to form. They came up with the idea of winding long lengths of glass fibers on a mandrel (a round bar made of wax or other material) so that the strands took the shape of the mandrel and were also very close together. As the fibers were fed onto the rotating mandrel, they were sprayed with liquid plastic. The plastic hardened and the wax mandrel was melted out. The resulting plastic-fiber case was very strong and as much as thirty per cent lighter than the metal case previously used. This meant that more propellant could be carried so the rocket could

101

travel hundreds of miles further. One of the first uses of this plastic case was in the second stage of the Polaris A-2 missile. The more advanced Polaris A-3 will have both first and second stage cases of plastic and will have a range of 2,500 nautical miles, twice the range of the first Polaris missiles carried by our nuclear missile submarines.

Many other present-day plastics are combinations of a resin binder and reinforcement of some sort. The reinforcing material may be thin fibers of glass, called fiber-glass, or fibers of ceramics or other kinds of material, including high-strength plastics. The resin is a plastic which is usually stored in a liquid state and then poured around the reinforcement. The resin gives the plastic its shape and also binds the reinforcing fibers together.

Plastics come in other forms as well. One major class is the thin film, examples of which are the clear rolls of wrapping paper, such as Saran Wrap, and cellophane. Still other kinds of plastic sheets are used as backing for photographic film. Another way in which plastics are used is in the form of foam. Synthetic sponges and foam cushions are examples of plastic foam.

The great length of polymer molecules permits scientists to make an almost infinite number of plastics. By varying the kinds of atoms attached at different points in the chain, and by changing the chain length, the interaction of one chain with another can be changed. The product of each minute change is a material with different properties. As a result, it's far

Example of the great strides scientists have made in development of nonmetallic materials is glass filament winding. Here continuous strands of coated glass fibers are wound on a rotating mandrel to form a Polaris rocket case. This case is much lighter than the metal case used in earlier versions of this Navy missile and has helped greatly increase the missile's range.

more difficult to discuss different kinds of plastics than different kinds of metals. It would take page after page of a whole series of books just to list the names of all the plastics studied thus far by research people. Even if we printed such a list, many new plastics would have been invented by the time the list was a few months old.

However, we can mention the names of a few of the

major classes of plastics. These include epoxy, polyester, polystyrene, urethane, phenolic, silicone, vinyl, melamine, acrylic, polyamide, and polypropylene. Each of these names covers a class of anywhere from dozens to hundreds of different plastics.

Epoxy compounds are widely used as tool and die material. An epoxy die might be used to shape a piece of sheet steel. The steel sheet is placed in the lower epoxy die in a huge press. Then the epoxy die is brought down on the steel with thousands of pounds of force, making the sheet change into the shape of the die.

Phenolics are very versatile plastics that can be made in a wide range of beautiful colors with various patterns in their surface. They are widely used as table tops and other surface decorations.

Polyethylene has a waxy feel and is used in protective jackets for electrical wire.

The trade name for the polyamides is Nylon.

Polyesters are used as the resins holding the glass fibers together in such things as boat hulls and automobile bodies.

Acrylics with their excellent optical properties are used in transparent, shatterproof glass. In the form of fibers, acrylics also are used in many of the latest fashions. The trade name for acrylic fibers is Orlon.

Urethane foams, in recent years, have helped provide vastly improved insulation for buildings, railroad refrigerator cars, and trucks. In a typical case, a layer of resin material is put down and just the right amount of another plastic poured over it. A chemical reaction takes place and the combined material foams up and hardens, leaving a material with millions of airholes, similar in structure to a household sponge. The difference is that the plastic foams of the urethane type are strong and rigid, not spongy. The shape of the foam can be controlled by having the reaction occur between whatever limits are desired. It can be foamed in place between the beams of a house just by spraying it on. Thus the walls of a house can be insulated in a fraction of the time needed to nail or staple on conventional insulating batts.

A measure of the great advances in plastics is their use in many extreme situations. A new plastic was recently developed to line the throat of rocket engine nozzles. The plastic uses a self-cooling technique to withstand temperatures of up to 10,000 degrees Fahrenheit. At such temperatures, tungsten, the metal with the highest melting point, would melt away in seconds. Other plastics are widely used as *ablative* protections for re-entry space vehicles. These plastics carry off heat by *ablating*. This means they burn or erode away at a slow rate so that the heat is used up in burning the plastic. In this way, the heat won't reach the main metal surface of the spacecraft underneath the plastic. The most widely used plastics for this purpose are epoxy and phenolic compounds reinforced with high-temperature fibers. The fibers usually are asbestos, high-silica glass, or graphite.

Engineers are also designing complete homes made

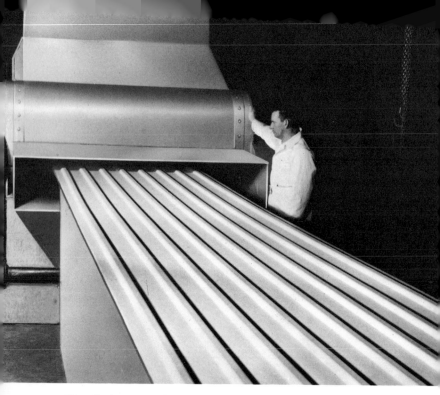

Plastic houses of tomorrow will be insect-resistant and will never need painting. Here a 48-inch-wide panel for such a house is extruded from a special machine.

of plastic. One type just announced is a pre-cut vacation home that can be put up in ten hours by a six-man crew on a prepared concrete base. The beams, tie rods, and other support members are pre-shaped by pressing (extruding) hot plastic through dies. The roof is made from sections of plastic "sandwich." The sandwich consists of inner and outer plastic skins bonded to core sections. These cores are made of thin strips of plastic put together in a pattern like that of a honeycomb. Insulation for the entire house is provided by foamed-in-place urethane plastic. This type of home, engineers

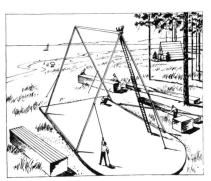

Artist's sketches show steps in assembling a vacation home of pre-cut plastic. The house is erected on a previously poured concrete slab and special plastic foam used between the beams and under the roof surfaces for insulation.

point out, not only has excellent insulation for all types of climates, but it also is very resistant to fire and not subject to rot, mildew, or termites. The plastic house never needs repainting and can be cleaned inside and out with a garden hose.

Still other kinds of houses designed from plastics are space huts. Hughes Aircraft has designed a canned hut which is made of foamed-in-place plastics that foam into a rigid structure on being exposed to sunlight. The material in this case is a polyurethane plastic that will foam only in a vacuum. In one test at Wright Patterson

Air Force Base, a seven-foot-high circular hut was made by opening a can of plastic inside a special vac-

"Instant furniture" — forerunner of canned goods of tomorrow are these foamed-plastic space items. Opening cans of special plastic in a vacuum causes the plastic to foam into, in one case, an "igloo" and, in the other, a chair.

Hughes Aircraft

All-plastic zippers made of Delrin are replacing metal ones in many of today's fashions. Zippers can be made in a wide range of colors.

uum chamber with special heating lamps used to simulate sunlight. At the same time, another can was opened that contained plastic pre-shaped so it would foam into a chair. These plastic items are perfect for use on the moon which has little or no atmosphere. Other kinds of plastics could be found, researchers note, that would foam into place only inside planetary atmospheres such as those found on Mars or Venus.

One of the most recent major advances in commercial plastics is Du Pont's Delrin resin. This plastic, made from formaldehyde, has a strength close to that of aluminum and zinc. With this kind of strength, Delrin has been used instead of metal in hundreds of places from parts of irons and all types of gears to umbrella ribs and complete zippers for clothes.

It's obvious that plastics have come a very long way

in just a short period of time. But scientists are sure that they have only scratched the surface of the potential of these materials.

The major effort in laboratories today is to get a much better understanding of exactly how plastics are made. We need to know the way in which the atoms and molecules are held together. Scientists are studying the energy bonds or internal forces which keep particles from separating from each other.

Despite their startling successes with plastics, chemists and physicists know little about these materials. As Stanford Research Institute scientists point out: "It may appear that all that's needed is to go into the laboratory and make materials for whatever specific use. We can talk quite glibly about the structure-property relationships in polymers and the 'molecular engineering' that can create these new materials. But the truth is that most polymeric materials were the result of a trial and error search — make a hundred polymers, shape them into a test article (a fabric, a film, or molded object) and see how it performs in use. Maybe it works, or maybe it doesn't. If not, make another hundred polymers and try them."

Of course, scientists have a general idea, from experience, which combinations probably will lead to the properties wanted in a given case. What they don't have are exact ways to figure out how to shape the polymer molecules to give just the right material. If scientists can find out these basic relationships, they can come up with polymers vastly better than the best used today, in much less time. Once researchers find out how to arrange polymers to fit any specific need, then the use of plastics will probably expand five or ten times over the tremendous volume of today.

To give just a few examples, scientists are doing advanced work on various kinds of non-brittle glasses. A truck could roll over a pane of this glass and it would not even crack.

Wide range of shapes and sizes made from reinforced plastics is shown in this panorama.

Lamtex

Another broad area of research is in basic food technology. Most foods are made up of polymers produced in nature. Knowledge of polymers will let scientists rearrange the way in which plants grow. Stanford Research Institute suggests it may be possible to grow plants which will contain proteins of a quality as good as those found in meats. This would make a rich source of high-quality protein available at a low price. Other plants could be made to produce more edible parts and less waste portions. This would mean more food for mankind from the same amount of farm land.

An even more exciting area of study is that involving health and disease. Scientists have begun to realize that much of the human body, and the germs and viruses that aid or attack it, is actually made of polymer compounds. Every function of the body depends on certain key "biological polymers." Thus the same basic understanding of polymers needed to make better plastic materials may also aid in the elimination of such diseases as cancer. This same understanding of polymers in humans can lead to longer, healthier lives for the generations to come. This area of study calls for the skills of polymer chemists, biologists, physicists, and medical specialists as well as materials experts.

Stanford Research Institute (SRI) scientists say that the molecules that make up the basic cells of our body depend on certain important polymer families of living systems. These are three in number: two acids and protein. Chemists call the two acids deoxyribonucleic acid and ribonucleic acid, more often called DNA and

RNA. Protein, the stuff of which cells and body structural tissues are made, is a polymer synthesized in part of the body cells. The DNA polymer is the storehouse of information on just how cells should reproduce themselves and how the cells must interact with one another. The RNA polymer has the job of taking this information to the right place in the cells and assembling the right materials to make the protein.

Scientists have only a rough idea of how all these things work, but they know that flaws in the polymers or in the way they act together can cause illness and various mental defects. "Essentially," say SRI scientists, "we can trace all diseases or disorders back to the molecular level — and to a particular molecule, the DNA one, which either misdirects the cell activity [because of some change in the DNA makeup] or prevents a particular cellular activity" because the required DNA molecule is not present.

This knowledge has already helped doctors save many children from wasted lives. At one time, it was thought that a child born mentally retarded was a hopeless case. Now, if the condition is caught early enough, doctors can do something about it. It has been discovered that one particular type of DNA molecule is missing in most of these cases. This molecule normally converts one kind of acid to a different type of acid. If the proper DNA molecule isn't there, the unconverted acid causes damage to the brain. By finding this out early enough in a child's life, doctors can supply the right kind of diet to prevent taking in the harm-

113

ful acid, thus preventing brain damage and permitting normal cell growth.

Going one step further, scientists have found that many of the harmful viruses and bacteria are also polymers. By knowing the basic theory of all polymers, they can develop special plastic compounds to destroy the disease germs. More important, this approach looks as if it can avoid the harmful "side effects" occasionally caused by today's antibiotics. There are great hopes that not only will such scourges as cancer be eliminated by polymer chemistry, but also that complete immunity to all kinds of disease, including the common cold, can be given all human beings.

Sometime in the future, too, these new polymer studies may teach scientists how to slow down the aging process so people will be active and healthy for many more years than at present. If this should come true, then the science of plastics may not only make man's life infinitely more interesting and enjoyable, it may also indeed be the long-sought "Fountain of Youth."

7

MATERIALS FOR THE NUCLEAR AGE

THE HUGE MUSHROOM cloud that spread out over the ruins of Hiroshima and Nagasaki is symbolic of the age in which we live. The power of the atom is an awesome thing, but it can furnish much that is good and useful for man instead of widespread destruction. In fact, the dread of atomic warfare may, after all, make world-wide wars a thing of the past. It is possible that concentration on peaceful uses of atomic power of almost unlimited energy and the availability nuclear reaction can finally free all people from poverty.

Nuclear energy may have come along at just the right time. Man is rapidly using up all the oil, coal, and other fuels he has found in nature. In a few hundred years, or even less, man will be hard put to find natural fuel to light his home or run his electrical equipment. But from a few pounds of nuclear fuel man can get enough energy to light hundreds of homes for years.

The great efficiency of nuclear energy can make

large-scale exploration of other planets feasible. Rocket engines using conventional chemical fuels would be impractical. An engine capable of carrying a crew of astronauts to Mars would have to weigh nine million pounds. It would be difficult, perhaps impossible, to assemble such a ship in orbit. If it were not launched from orbit it would have to be much heavier. A nuclear engine capable of the same trip would weigh only ten per cent as much, or 900,000 pounds (assembled in orbit).

There is much to be done in the materials field before nuclear space engines can be used. The use of nuclear energy makes demands on materials different from any ever before encountered in the history of science. Temperatures in some of the parts of a chemical rocket system are sometimes as high as 10,000 degrees Fahrenheit. The heat anticipated in nuclear systems makes chemical rockets seem almost cool by comparison. The temperatures go into the millions and even the tens of millions of degrees. Special fuels, some of which do not appear in nature, also are required to make nuclear reactors function.

Radiation also becomes a factor in nuclear energy systems. Materials in a nuclear system must shield human passengers from dangerous invisible rays and the materials themselves must not be affected by radiation from the nuclear core of the engine. Radiation can have strange effects on ordinary materials. It can cause some materials to expand. Such expansion could be dangerous, for if a moving part should swell and jam in place, the whole system could break down, leaving a space ship drifting and helpless. Radiation can also make some materials weaker. These weakened materials might fail under ordinary loads.

Strangely enough, there are some materials which grow stronger under exposure to radiation. This is true of many metals. It is true also of some plastics, although plastics usually are weakened by radiation. This fact already has been used in industry to turn out better materials for everyday use. Several companies expose a polyethylene plastic to radiation and get a much

Good nuclear materials will pave the way for the conquest of space. As this National Aeronautics and Space Administration comparison shows, a nuclear Mars rocket assembled in earth orbit weighs only about 10 per cent what a chemical rocket would.

NASA

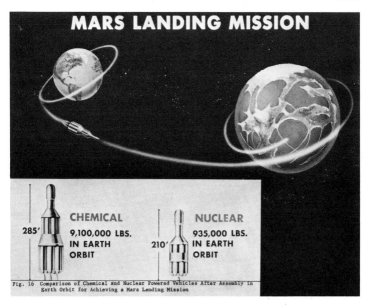

Fig. 16 Comparison of Chemical and Nuclear Powered Vehicles After Assembly in Earth Orbit for Achieving a Mars Landing Mission

better insulating material to put around electrical wire.

An additional consideration in working with nuclear power is the length of time it takes materials exposed to radiation to lose radioactivity. Some materials become radioactive only while they are near a nuclear source. A short time after they are taken away from the radiation area they return to normal and are safe to handle. Other substances absorb radiation and stay dangerously radioactive for years.

The term scientists use to compare the time a particular material remains radioactive after exposure to nuclear energy is "half-life." This is the time it takes for the radioactivity of a given amount of a material to fall to half its initial value. Half-lives vary widely. For instance, a form of the element cobalt known as cobalt-60 has a half-life of 5.3 years. Zinc-65 has a half-life of 245 days. On the other hand, nickel has a half-life of only 2.5 hours, copper 12.8 hours, and aluminum-27 only 2.3 minutes.

In designing equipment for work near a nuclear power source, the materials with high half-lives must be avoided and those with low half-lives used. In addition, care must be taken that the alloying elements used in low-half-life materials also have a low half-lives. Thus while aluminum alloyed with copper would be a good material to use, aluminum alloyed with zinc must be kept away from reactors.

However, if short half-lives are important for materials surrounding a nuclear source, this is not true of the heart of the nuclear device, the radioactive core.

The core contains the nuclear fuel. Fuel material, to be efficient, must be capable of supporting a nuclear reaction for long periods of time. It is the discovery of ways to produce and use a good nuclear fuel material that makes atomic energy important today. This material, of course, has become almost a byword for atomic energy. Its name is uranium.

Uranium was found in 1789 by Martin Heinrich Klaproth. He discovered what he took to be a new metal while studying a sample of pitchblende material from Saxony in Germany. In 1781, Sir William Herschel, a great English scientist, had discovered the planet Uranus. In honor of this, Klaproth named his new "metal" uranium. However, time proved he had been wrong. He had not discovered the metal uranium, but a ceramic composition of it, uranium dioxide. In 1841, E. M. Peligot proved this and also isolated true uranium metal — a metal that has a shiny white color resembling that of polished steel. Metallic uranium, scientists found, was highly reactive. If a chunk of it is dropped into a container of water, it will decompose the water.

Uranium played a major role in the late 1800s in work that led to the discovery of radioactivity. This happened in 1896 when the French scientist H. A. Becquerel was trying to find a connection between X-rays and the fact that a certain kind of uranium salt glowed in the dark. He wrapped a piece of photographic film in black paper so sunlight could not get through to expose it. Then he glued a crystal of uranium salt on the outside of the black paper. When the film was developed, it came out black, indicating that it had been exposed. The sunlight could not have done this. Therefore, the test proved that the uranium salt sent out radiation which could penetrate paper. His discovery started many other scientists working on the problem. The crowning achievement was made by Pierre and Marie Curie when they extracted the radio-active element radium from pitchblende. Soon scientists found that many other elements — cadmium, bismuth, iodine, mercury — also emitted radioactive rays.

Strangely enough, although uranium played such a major role in early radioactive work, it was thought to be of little use. It was not until studies of radioactive particles led to the discovery of atomic energy that uranium was "re-discovered." Many people in the scientific community were astonded by the discovery of radioactivity, but they quickly realized how important this could be. The fact that certain atoms — without outside aid — could send out electrically charged particles that could affect a photographic plate meant that energy was being liberated. This indicated that there might be an easier way of getting energy to do useful work than conventional electric power systems. The big question was whether materials could be found that would send out this energy on a large enough and cheap enough basis to make the process practical.

All through the early 1900s, more and more scientists studied the problem. They tried to find out as much as they could about the atoms that made up radioactive materials. Intensive study led to the knowledge that different types of radioactive particles existed. They next discovered the various types of energy given off by these particles. As knowledge built up step-by-step over the years, scientists finally were led to discover the possibility that certain particles could provide a nuclear "chain reaction." This was realized independently and almost at the same time by a number of scientists in different parts of the world just before World War II. These scientists included H. von Halban, Frederic Joliot, and L. Kowarski in France and Enrico Fermi in the United States. The idea of a chain reaction offered a way to make a small amount of fuel give off large amounts of energy for long periods of time.

A chain reaction is a little like having a table full of marbles. If you hit one, you can cause it to bounce into another, causing the next marble to hit still another one. A nuclear chain reaction is started by bombarding the nucleus of a radioactive type of atom and splitting it. This is called nuclear fission. The split parts of the atom then split other atoms and these atoms split still others. The important difference between the bouncing marbles and the collision of atoms is that the splitting of an atom causes a great amount of heat to be given off. In atomic power plants, this heat is used to do work. It might be used to turn water into steam. The steam then is used to turn a turbine wheel. The turning wheel can rotate a ship's propeller or cause a generator to produce electricity.

The first new series of materials to be intensively studied was fuel materials. Plain uranium wasn't good enough, but scientists found that there were a number of different kinds of uranium. In fact, research showed that many elements could be found in more than one atomic form. These different forms were called isotopes. The difference between one isotope of uranium and another is a very slight variation in atomic weight. Uranium-235 has an atomic weight of 235 while uranium-238 has an atomic weight of 238. The material used in the first atomic bombs was mainly uranium-235. There was one drawback. Uranium-235 is much rarer than uranium-238. The problem was that uranium-238 can't be split as easily as the uranium-235 form. If only some way could be found to use uranium-238 for atomic energy, scientists thought, the cost of fuel could be greatly reduced, paving the way for doing many more things with the atom.

The result of their thinking was the creation, for the first time in history, of artificial elements. Until the 1940s, all materials in the world were based on a certain fixed set of elements. These elements could be combined to give many materials with new properties, but the elements themselves remained unchanged. The new, artificial elements are made by carefully exposing natural uranium elements to radioactivity. The first element made in this way was produced by American scientists E. M. McMillan and P. H. Abelson in 1940 and was called neptunium. Many other new

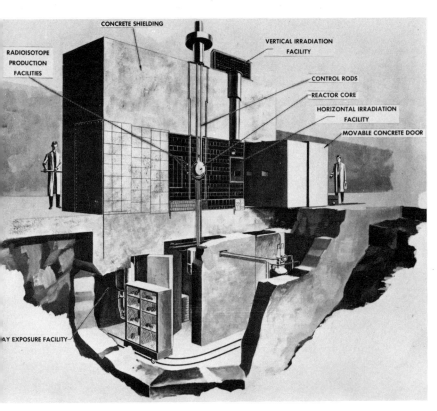

Nuclear technology calls for many new developments in materials. A typical atomic installation is this 50,000-watt reactor built for biological research at Walter Reed hospital.

elements have since been made. They include curium, einsteinium, fermium, mendelevium, nobelium, berkelium, technetium, promethium, astatine and francium.

By far the most important element made in this way is plutonium. Plutonium is made from plentiful uranium-238 and is split easily by all kinds of radioactive particles. Scientists finally had found a way to use the more common types of uranium to obtain atomic energy.

Most of today's nuclear reactors use uranium-235 or plutonium as fuel. Of course, there are continuing studies being made to get still better fuel materials. For some uses, scientists have found it better to use ceramic compounds made from uranium and plutonium rather than the pure metals. Examples of these ceramic fuels are plutonium dioxide, uranium dioxide, and uranium carbide.

The discovery of cheaper and more plentiful fuels was an important step in making atomic power available for peaceful uses, but it was only one step. Nuclear reactors need careful control, for they generate heat through a chain reaction in the fuel. This is the same principle which causes an atomic explosion. Scientists designed their reactors to control the chain reaction through the use of a moderator, a material which is added to the fuel to make sure the reaction takes place slowly and evenly rather than explosively. One good moderator is water. In many of the large nuclear power stations which now give electricity to some of our cities, the uranium fuel is placed in a deep pool of water. Such plants are sometimes called "swimming pool" reactors.

Swimming pool reactors are excellent as long as a great deal of water is available, but scientists knew that if they wanted to make small nuclear engines to run submarines or spaceships, they had to find a different kind of moderator. Such a material acts as a kind of nuclear brake. High-energy particles strike against the moderator and slow down, but the moderator must not absorb particles and stop the reaction. Very few materials are good "brakes."

It was not until many hours of laboratory tests had been performed that it was found that graphite and beryllium could do the job. It was further learned that beryllium could be used in the form of beryllium oxide, a ceramic.

To know that certain materials will meet particular requirements is one thing, but to produce the materials in the right grades and in large amounts is something quite different.

Graphite had been used for years in pencil "leads," but large parts had to be made from graphite for nuclear purposes. Pencil graphite in large pieces is very weak, so new, stronger graphite had to be developed. Graphite used in reactors also had to be much purer than that used in pencils.

Beryllium also needed improvement. This unusual metal had been used for years in small amounts in electrical contacts, but making large parts from it had never been done before. As mentioned earlier, scientists of the Atomic Energy Commission first found new sources of beryllium and then devised ways to make extremely pure beryllium in large sections, improved the metal's ductility, and eliminated dangers from its poisonous dust and vapors.

Today, the AEC is sponsoring work on beryllium oxide, the form in which most beryllium is now used in advanced nuclear projects. A major need is to make this ceramic free of pinholes and therefore stronger.

Scientists in AEC-sponsored projects have come up with a special fabrication method known as semi-continuous hot pressing. In this method, beryllium oxide is formed in a die under continuous very high pressure. While this is done, heating coils around the die keep the temperature up to several hundred degrees. This has resulted in production of large, single pieces of the material for use in nuclear cores with several times the strength of normal beryllium oxide parts.

In addition to the fuel and moderator of a nuclear reactor, there is a third major part in a workable nuclear system. This is the control rod. The control rod makes it possible to turn a reactor on or off. A control rod is made of a material that will absorb nuclear particles and keep them from striking other particles. It shuts off the chain reaction. Control rods inside a nuclear core act a little like a sponge. The instant the rods are removed, the high-energy particles are free to strike others and the core can then turn out heat energy.

Only a few materials in the world can be used for controlling a nuclear reaction. Most of these are extreme rarities. For instance, the list includes: zirconium hydride, boron nitride, hafnium oxide, europium oxide, gadolinium oxide, samarium oxide, and such metals as hafnium.

Hafnium was one of the materials developed for the nuclear submarine program. In 1949-50, this metal was as rare as uranium had been a few years earlier. Navy researchers working under Admiral Rickover and AEC specialists were faced with the problem of finding a material so scarce it cost thousands of dollars a pound. At the same time they also had to develop another material for another part of the system that was even scarcer. This was the metal zirconium, costing, at the time, about $450,000 a pound. Zirconium was about the only metal that could be used efficiently for the tubing in which the cooling material flowed around the nuclear core. Temperatures around the reactor are 700 to 1,000 degrees Fahrenheit. The coolant must remove heat very rapidly or the core could destroy itself. Special, very corrosive cooling fluids which would eat through most metals must be used. Zirconium proved to be suitable for carrying this fluid. Researchers then became lucky. They found that one of the impurities that had to be removed from zirconium ore was hafnium. Thus when they found large enough amounts of zirconium to bring its price down to a reasonable amount, they also had a source of hafnium.

For nuclear space powerplants, coolant requirements are even higher than for ground systems. In space engines, the faster heat can be radiated away from the nuclear area the smaller the system can be, and size is always an important consideration in spacecraft. This calls for fluids with even faster heat-absorption properties than coolants used in most current ground systems. The only materials meeting these requirements are certain kinds of liquid metals. These liquid metals are sodium, potassium, lithium, rubidium, and cesium.

Sometimes combinations are used — particularly an alloy of sodium and potassium. (In some ground-based reactors of the newer kinds, called "fast" reactors, heat must also be taken away much more rapidly than water will do it and here too a sodium-potassium liquid metal is used.) These are metals than can only be contained in tubing or tanks made of some of the "metals of tomorrow" — columbium and tantalum are the two most likely to be used for this purpose.

Space powerplants actually use two fuels. First there is the nuclear fuel of the core which provides a great amount of heat. This heat is then used to make a rocket fuel, such as liquid hydrogen, expand rapidly enough through a nozzle to give rocket thrust. Hot hydrogen presents another major problem, since most of the high-temperature metals will absorb it and hydrogen, when absorbed, makes most metals brittle and causes them to crack easily. Graphite is a likely material for nuclear rocket nozzles since it has the rare property of actually becoming stronger as the temperature increases. In addition, it does not become any more brittle if it takes in hydrogen. However, above a certain temperature hydrogen will wear away the graphite surface. Scientists are searching for a thin protective coating, perhaps some type of ceramic, to put on the graphite surface to prevent hydrogen erosion.

In the future there may be a source of energy even greater than nuclear fission, or splitting the atom. This source is called fusion, or forcing together two separate atoms to form one single atom. The energy given off during fusion dwarfs even the astounding energy of present-day nuclear fission. However, very high pressures and temperatures of ten million to 100 million degrees are required to fuse two atoms together.

How can this be done? Certainly such temperatures would vaporize any materials we know of today in less than a second. The answer is that the hot fuel must be kept from ever touching the container wall. One way to do this is to line the reactor area with a series of extremely powerful magnets. These magnets send out strong magnetic forces that not only squeeze the fuel atoms together, but also literally hold the multi-million-degree fuel "plasmas" in mid-air. Even so, a tremendously difficult materials problem must be solved. The stronger the magnetic forces become, the greater the chance that the magnet itself will be torn apart. New magnet materials and special magnet designs will be needed to contain the energy of fusion. Scientists have not yet succeeded in creating fusion which can be controlled, but they are making progress. Temperatures of over a million degrees have been achieved. Some fusion on a very small laboratory scale has also been done.

It's a little early to talk much about specific materials, since fusion on a workable scale is ten to twenty years away. We can say that fusion fuel will probably be some form of hydrogen. Deuterium, also called "heavy" hydrogen because every molecule of the gas has an atomic mass almost twice that of ordinary hydrogen, may be used. Another form of hydrogen called tritium is also a possibility for use as fusion fuel.

When nuclear fusion materials are perfected and fusion energy becomes available on a practical scale, it will be a breakthrough much more important than anything which has happened in the history of science.

8

MATERIALS
BECOMES A SCIENCE

IN TWO MAJOR manufacturing plants, General Electric, Schenectady, New York, and de Beers, Ltd., South Africa, there is an area where long rows of machines are busily at work. A visitor would see little of what the machines are doing, but he might be startled now and then by a sudden, muffled roar from one or more of them.

Outwardly these machines are no more impressive than any of the other tools in the factories, but these are not ordinary machines. They symbolize the growth of materials as a science. For centuries during the Middle Ages, alchemists searched for ways of changing common metals such as lead into precious gold or silver. They never succeeded, but in these two widely separated modern factories, the alchemists' dreams have come true. The machines in these plants are busily making graphite, the source of ordinary pencil lead, into synthetic diamonds.

Prime example of tailored materials are these man-made diamonds, produced in ultra-high-pressure machines.

Making materials to order, changing or improving the properties of all kinds of materials, and production of completely new man-created materials are the result of the materials revolution.

Within recent years, a flood of new materials has poured out of research and development laboratories. At one time it was thought to be an unusual year if a few dozen new alloys came into being. In the past decade, over 10,000 new alloys have been added to materials catalogues. Dr. L. W. Van Vlack, Professor of Materials Engineering at the University of Michigan, has pointed out that there were 100 times as many types of glass in 1950 as there were in 1900. By 1975 there will be well over 4,000 times as many kinds of glass as at the turn of the century. In plastics and rubber compounds, the number of types by 1975 will be over 10,000 times that of 1900, and similar ratios, says Van Vlack, hold for ceramics.

As fast as new materials have become available, the demands by engineers have outstripped them. The many new materials actually started this cycle by giving the engineers the basis to design scores of new things. We see the results of new designs around us every day. Automatic washers, miniature radios and television sets based on transistors and other semiconductor materials, flameproof non-fading curtains from glass fibers, and copying machines that turn out duplicates of printed material in seconds are all made from new materials. In addition, such complex things as jet airplanes, missiles, and atomic energy have come as a result of the materials revolution.

Once new materials were available, the human mind rapidly developed ever more far-ranging ideas. The more advanced these ideas became, the more difficult it was for materials researchers — divided as they were into separate little groups in ceramics, metals, chemicals, plastics, and other fields — to keep up with them.

For example, tungsten has an amazing temperature capability allowing it to withstand heat up to 5,000 degrees Fahrenheit without failing. But the design of more powerful rockets calls for more powerful fuels which in turn create higher temperatures in rocket exhaust nozzles. Already these temperatures promise to go well beyond the melting point of tungsten.

Engineers in atomic energy are making demands for materials which must meet requirements equally severe. Special materials must withstand radiation without failure and prevent radiation from leaking out to pollute the surroundings. Additional fuels are needed in atomic energy as are materials which can survive temperatures hundreds of times hotter than those produced by chemical-powered engines.

H. R. Clauser, editor of the publication "Materials in Design Engineering," points out that not only in space flight, automation and atomic energy, but also "in the less glamorous fields of industrial and consumer products, materials are now recognized as the critical factor that determines cost, quality and performance."

Dr. W. O. Baker, vice president of research at Bell Telephone Laboratories, summed up the significance of materials in our present age this way: "Materials as never before must be the means through which man realizes his dreams of well-being on earth or, failing that, liberation into space.

"In every manufacturing field, materials have become the major consideration in planning, designing and producing products. There is hardly an industry that is not searching for new or better materials to meet increasingly severe service conditions, to improve product performance, and to lower materials or production costs."

MATERIALS BECOMES A SCIENCE

The way to close the increasing gap between what current materials can do and what future designs need, scientists decided, was to create a new science of materials. Materials science is the study of every material known to man. As we've noted, up to now materials have been subdivided into several major groups. In addition, each main group has many subdivisions. For instance, there are ferrous, or iron-containing, metals and non-ferrous metals, which contain no iron. A major subdivision of chemicals is plastics. There are, of course, many other divisions of materials. Each of these groups has tended to become a separate area, each with its own specialists. The engineers and scientists in each area looked only at their own groups of materials, rarely considering materials in other groups in their studies.

As time went on, physicists realized that all materials are made up of a limited number of types of matter such as atoms, electrons, and other particles. The way these basic bits of matter are joined together determines the properties of a material. The composition of materials might be compared to the way building blocks are used in construction. If the blocks are put together in one way, they become a church. If they are arranged in another way, the result is an apartment house. Still a different combination might provide a bridge or a courthouse.

Scientists came to understand that by studying the minute bits of matter in all materials they would learn how completely new systems could be devised. It would be possible to make diamonds from carbon, or gold from mercury. More important, combinations of all types of materials could be made to give new materials vastly better properties than anything man had known before.

The first requirement of the new science was better instruments to study the basic atomic structure. Over the years, precise instruments were devised to look into the heart of the atom, such as X-ray diffraction equipment, the chromatograph, and the spectrograph. These instruments project on a screen a series of lines which vary either in shade of color or in line width. From the lines, a scientist can determine what a given atomic structure is like. Such machines can be designed to show how atoms interact with one another and the changes in energy when atoms strike each other.

Special high-power microscopes were invented to help the materials researcher. These make it possible for him to see in greater detail the structure of each material. Very precise measuring equipment also has been invented to make it possible to find out the amount of energy generated when elements react or combine with each other.

From work with these instruments, scientists found that the binding forces holding the minute particles of solid materials together were of the same nature for all materials. The same set of rules applied whether metals were combined with other metals, ceramics with metals, plastics with ceramics, or if any other combina-

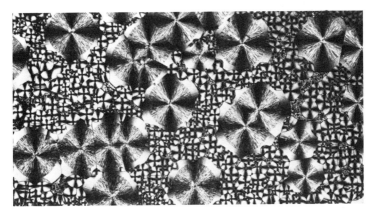

General Electric

Similarity of structure in metal and plastic is shown above. Polarized light micrographs show crystallites growing in polymer (top) and cast iron.

tion were made. Pictures of the structure of materials were magnified hundreds and thousands of times and compared. Such micrographs indicated that the same kind of crystal growths was present in all kinds of materials (see photograph).

Methods of working on the atom or assembly of atoms are as important as devices which allow us to "see" the atom. More and more mechanical methods, from the first "atom-smasher" or cyclotron to atomic fission processes and high pressure technology, are providing ways of doing this. At the same time, many new ways of producing complex materials have come into existence. Luckily, many of the methods that can be used to study basic materials properties can also be used in forming and producing new materials.

Materials of tomorrow will be vastly better than even today's advanced metals, ceramics, and plastics, thanks to scientific studies of the basic makeup of all matter. Shown here is a model of a diamond crystal used in such work.

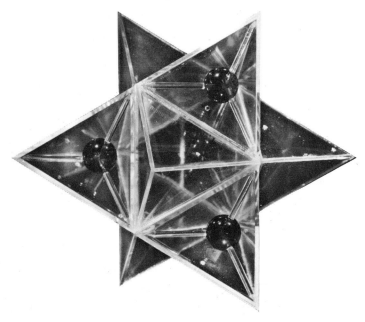

A good example is the case of synthetic diamonds. Scientists have discovered how to build machines which will deliver previously unheard of pressures — from one to three million pounds on every inch of material surface. This is the equivalent of the pressure which would be exerted by a granite column 400 miles high — or over 3,000 times the height of the Washington Monument.

This much pressure is needed to overcome the tremendous resistance to change of many atomic structures. Special anvils were developed and ways found to deliver massive hammer blows against specimens in these anvils. One method makes use of hydraulic fluid to force a piston against the anvil. Another approach, which produces very high pressure for a short time, is to set off a compact charge of explosive against the piston.

Machines capable of producing such great pressures may be used to manufacture special garnets and rubies with very important electronic properties, as well as diamonds. Synthetic jade also has been produced under high pressure, as well as samples of new kinds of plastics. Many basic studies of the properties of materials can be made using pressure machines. Although work in this area is still in its very early stages, it is expected that many materials with completely new properties can be built. Many scientists feel that the ordinary physical and chemical properties of many common elements will be so changed that they will be new elements and a new periodic table will be required.

The periodic table, which was perfected by Meyer and Mendeleev about 1869, lists all the possible elements, such as lead, carbon, gold, silver, etc., according to their physical and chemical properties. The table was so near perfection that it accurately predicted many new elements then unknown but since discovered. Each newly discovered element proved to have the properties forecast in the table. As recently as twenty-five years ago, many scientists believed it would never have to be redrawn. Now a complete revision seems likely within the lifetime of today's high school student. This is another result of the growth of materials science.

Many other radically new developments are playing major roles in materials science. The area of study called *ultrasonics* is one of these. Ultrasonics involves the use of sound waves to perform many tasks, from providing superclean material surfaces to welding dissimilar materials together. In industry, ultrasonic machines are being used to clean very delicate pieces of material, such as extremely accurate gyroscope parts used in the guidance systems of submarines and missiles. In materials research, it's also important in many cases to make sure that all impurities are removed from a surface so that any test measurements made will truly represent those of the material tested. Again, ultrasonic cleaners can be used.

Sound waves are a form of mechanical energy and can cause an object to vibrate. The vibration can shake dirt particles loose from a surface. Sound causes the eardrum to vibrate, which is why you can hear. This energy can be used in many ways to determine the internal properties of materials. The vibration of atoms inside a structure due to ultrasound can be detected by sensing devices to tell, for instance, how much elasticity (that is, ability to bend or deform) a material has. Ultrasonics can also be used to observe how heat travels through various materials or determine how well a mixture of several materials is being compounded.

The use of very high energy beams of light is another new approach to working with materials. An example of this is a device called the *laser*. The word laser stands for the initials of the phrase: light amplification by simulated emission of radiation. The laser uses a very special crystal, made from synthetic ruby, to produce a very intense beam of light. This crystal is made by the ultra high pressure method discussed earlier. A light beam from a laser is so concentrated that it hardly spreads out at all as it travels from the source.

As a result, a very high concentration of light energy can be focused on a small spot. The energy involved is about four million watts per square inch. The method can be compared to the way a beam of sunlight focused on a spot with a hand magnifying glass can cause an object to burn. However, the energy from the laser is thousands of times greater than that from the magnifying glass. Therefore, it's easy to burn through the strongest metal or ceramic in a flickering of an eyelash. It also permits performing many tests on the atomic structure of a material. Work with the laser is in its infancy, but it already is being used to weld together some of the materials which are extremely hard to join by ordinary methods. Since it can rapidly vaporize materials and this vapor can then be deposited on various surfaces, the laser can be used to provide pure samples for materials research, as well as special coatings, odd shaped parts, and other items.

Very high vacuums are also being achieved for use in materials research. The air around us contains stray chemicals, dust, various gases, and other matter that can combine with a molten material. Impurities, even in small quantities, can make it difficult or impossible for a researcher to discover the basic properties of a material. To eliminate impurities, the scientist can melt the material, draw off the impurities, and then form the material in a high vacuum. After the material solidifies, it can be exposed to the open air and no new impurities will be able to penetrate the solid.

This pure material might have very special properties for conducting electric current. If the same material were melted and formed while exposed to the air, it would pick up impurities that would ruin its efficiency as a conductor of electricity. Vacuum as complete as that of outer space must be created for experiments with pure materials. Special pumping systems produce such vacuum and make possible amazing new types of electronic equipment.

In still another approach, streams of electrons are

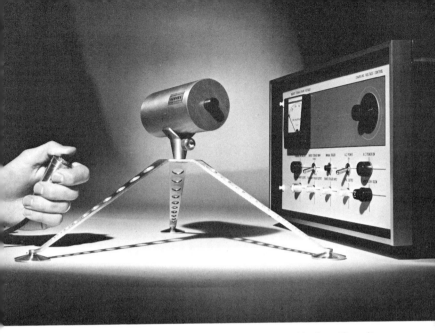

Small, one-pound laser on tripod prepares to emit its nearly parallel beam of "coherent" light in a test. One of the first commercial lasers, this unit and its accompanying power supply (right) will probably sell for less than $2500.

used to work on advanced materials. Devices called electron beam machines decompose matter and shoot a stream of very minute particles called electrons into a vacuum surrounded by magnetic coils. The coils focus the electrons and shoot beams of them at a target.

By varying the distance to the target and the energy in the beam, many different things can be done to materials. For instance, materials which cannot normally be welded together, such as a brittle ceramic and a refractory metal or one ceramic to another, can be welded with this device. Changing the arrangement of the device a little permits a scientist to use the beam

143

to cut holes finer than the width of a pin in glass, metal, or even diamonds. Electron beam melting also has produced the purest ingots of some metals ever made. From study of these pure ingots, researchers can obtain very accurate information on the metals and devise ways to make better parts from them.

Crystal growing is yet another new technology, and it is already of vital importance to the electronics industry.

Crystal growth begins with a minute bit of material called a *seed*. The seed is usually an almost perfect crystal of the material to be grown. A typical seed is perhaps 1/8 inch square. The seed is placed in a liquid pool of certain materials and pulled slowly through a series of magnetic coils. Crystals of the melt then form on the seed. It has been possible to grow large rods of materials such as silicon, one of the elements of which ordinary grains of sand are made. Ordinarily, silicon is very difficult to form in one piece. Using the new crystal-growing technique, it is possible to obtain silicon for many electronic devices such as transistors.

Most materials are made up of many very small crystals bound together in one way or another. Crystal growing permits making very large single crystals of a material. Rods of tungsten an inch or so in diameter and up to twelve inches long have been drawn as one big crystal. A rod the same size made from tungsten powder in a pressure mold would be composed of many, many tiny crystals of the metal. As we have seen, the single-crystal material often has very different properties from the multi-crystal form. Single crystal tungsten is much more efficient for some electronic uses.

Extreme vacuum, concentrated sound waves, powerful rays of light, and intense electron beams are some of the revolutionary new methods used to manipulate materials. There are other processes in use and more to come soon. The ultimate goal of materials researchers is to tailor materials to any demand, regardless of what it may be.

Dr. J. H. Holloman of General Electric Research Laboratories puts it this way. "The aircraft designer, like the designer of turbines, in company with the automobile designer join the designer of refrigerators in asking, 'What is the best material?' Each wants to know how to request the material and how it can be developed. He is not concerned with whether the material is metallic, ceramic or made of green cheese."

The engineer making plans for a hydroelectric plant to generate electricity to light homes and factories needs better materials for the blades of the huge electric turbines. The architect designing a new building doesn't really care if a material used in the building is metallic ceramic or plastic. All he's interested in is if it will do the job — take the load without collapsing, possibly look good and take a lot of punishment without wearing, and cost as little as possible. So too with the electronics engineer and just about every other materials user.

At the present time the engineer must examine hundreds of different materials in widely different categories to find what he wants. He must take what he can get. After looking at the properties of the various available materials, the designer compromises by picking the one that comes closest to his needs.

With the growth of materials science, this will all change. Instead of asking what's available, the person wanting a material will instead ask, What do I need? If it's a new carpet material, he will list how it will look and feel to the touch and how much wear it must take before wearing out. The list will then be given to the materials specialist who, with the aid of a computer, will figure out the elements that go into the material and the production methods needed. The result will be something that will do the job, no matter what the material is called. These tailored materials will be made in much the same way a cake is baked — a pinch of this, a pinch of that, a cup of something else will be mixed together and, presto, a special material will be born.

Before all this can be accomplished, people skilled in the overall science of materials will be needed. The great universities have begun to recognize this and revamp their courses. One of the first to do this, in 1952, was the University of Michigan, followed by the University of California at Berkeley and, more recently, California Institute of Technology. There is also a graduate center of materials sciences at Massachusetts Institute of Technology. All these schools used to have separate departments of metallurgy, ceramics, and chemistry. Now all these departments have been brought together as subdivisions of a new materials science section. Students can take courses leading to a degree in Materials Engineering. Recently, Stanford University announced it was building a brand new, multi-million-dollar Materials Science Lab embracing all aspects of materials. Eventually, it's expected that every major engineering and science school will do the same.

9

TAILORED MATERIALS

IMAGINE A RADIO so small it can fit on the head of a pin. The wrist-watch radio used by a comic-strip detective once was thought impossible, but working radios of this size already have been made. Still smaller radios not only are possible, they're inevitable.

Imagine a strand of material no bigger than a human air which could support the Empire State Building or the world's largest ocean liner in mid-air. There are materials coming that theoretically have the strength to do the job.

These stories represent just two of the advances that will come from the detailed application of tailored material research.

The area of research dealing with super-strength fine threads of material is called *whisker technology*. It has nothing to do with razor blade commercials on television. A few years ago, scientists discovered that under certain conditions, extremely fine whiskers of some materials could be grown on what were originally smooth surfaces. The way this is usually done is to treat the surface with certain kinds of chemicals while surrounding it with a special gas or vacuum envelope. These whiskers are much smaller in diameter than the finest human hair.

Scientists tested the properties of these whiskers and found some amazing things. The strength of a whisker of ordinary iron, for instance, was over a million pounds per square inch. This is a strength four or five times that of the strongest steel used today. Since then, further research has shown that whiskers can be made of materials other than metals. Scientists have made whiskers from many ceramics, including aluminum oxide, silicon carbide, and thorium oxide. The strength of some of the other whisker materials exceed even that of iron.

Of course, amazing as the properties of whiskers are, these materials still are mostly laboratory items and a long way from widespread use. The problem is that scientists can only grow small batches of whiskers an inch or at most a few inches long. Also, they can't yet be made cheaply or in great quantity. If whiskers many yards long could be made, a few of them twisted together could be used to pull a freight train. It would also be possible to weave cloth so strong that a high explosive shell could be fired at it and the cloth would not break.

It will take researchers many years to find out how to make long strands of super-strong hairs. When this happens, and if scientists also unlock the secret of making large sheets of metals or ceramics with whisker-like strengths, all present-day materials will be obsolete. The study of whiskers, how they form, and why they are so strong, once again involves the review of basic atomic structure. This type of research, as has been pointed out in previous chapters, is the key to the new science of tailored materials.

In the meantime, whisker research is having some immediate practical effects. Scientists are using knowledge gained from this work to make very small, high-strength bits of material in the form of short fibers or small pellets. While these materials have strengths far below that of whiskers, they are far stronger than if they were made in large amounts. Millions of these bits of strong materials can then be mixed into big batches of less strong materials. This approach results in the manufacture of new compositions with much better properties.

Two examples of this are Sintered Aluminum Powder (SAP) and the recently introduced TD Nickel. In the case of SAP, the ceramic aluminum oxide is dispersed throughout the aluminum metal. The resulting material has much greater strength at high temperatures than ordinary aluminum. The best alloys of conventional aluminum become soft and weak at temperatures over 500 to 600 degrees Fahrenheit. SAP, on the other hand, can withstand temperatures of more than 900 degrees. SAP also has much better strength than ordinary aluminum when exposed to radiation and is finding many uses in atomic energy.

TD Nickel, introduced by Du Pont, is a much newer material. The same principle is applied to nickel. The ceramic thorium oxide is mixed with the high strength metal. To do this successfully required precise knowledge of the grain structure of the metals involved. A special chemical process had to be found to assure extremely fine, uniform dispersion of the hard thorium oxide particles throughout the nickel. These ceramic particles are only a millionth of an inch in diameter. The combination of thorium oxide with nickel provides a material that will withstand temperatures of 1,600 to 2,400 degrees Fahrenheit. Pure nickel alone would not be usable at these temperatures.

What does thorium oxide do to make the nickel stronger? Scientists know that the many small grains or crystals that make up a metal are joined together haphazardly along lines called grain boundaries. As the temperature and/or the forces applied to the metal increase, the grains try to slide past each other along these lines. As they slide, the metal stretches out and becomes weaker. It's something like the way a piece of taffy will sag in the middle when it is stretched out. If small particles of hard material can be wedged between the crystals, the particles will tend to lock the grains together and keep them from sliding. The ceramic addition performs this role in the metal to provide vastly improved material.

Studies of the atomic structure of materials have led to other major achievements. For instance, in certain kinds of materials, the *ordering* of crystals or atoms will give the material much different properties. By *ordering*, we mean lining up the crystals in neat rows or special arrangements. An example of this is the *pyrolytic* materials. A pyrolitic material is one whose crystals have been ordered so that the material has a different set of properties along its length than it does along its width. One such pyrolitic material is made from graphite, which besides being used in pencil lead, also appears as ordinary soot or lumps of coal.

Greatly magnified pictures of normal graphite show the graphite crystals jumbled up and in no set pattern. Scientists decided to see what would happen if special production methods were invented to make ordered graphite. This means the graphite is made so that its crystals all point in the same general direction. This is done by passing hot gas streams containing carbon over specially prepared surfaces in a special chamber. The carbon settles out on the surface in long slender layers. The process is continued until the desired thickness of part is built up. The long, very thin carbon layers are now stacked one on top of the other like a large pile of papers. The boundary between each layer acts like a road-block to stop the passage of heat (or other forms of energy such as electricity) aimed at the top layer of the part. But the reverse is true of heat or electricity introduced into the end of the part. The long unbroken lengthwise layers have no boundaries — or at least far fewer ones — to prevent the flow of energy. This new material, then, has "directional" properties. In other words, it allows energy to pass easily in one direction but is very resistant to it in another.

A pyrolytic graphite heat shield is one example. A delicate piece of electric equipment might be placed on top of a sheet of this graphite and a blowtorch turned on the bottom of the sheet. This equipment might start to burn or at least stop running if its temperature went above about 160 degrees Fahrenheit. The blowtorch temperature is easily double this temperature. But because the pyrographite spreads the

Ordering of atomic structure is a key part of tailoring materials. These two magnified pictures of graphite show what ths means. At the top is shown ordinary graphite, with its crystals randomly scattered. At the bottom is shown new pyrographite, a material whose crystals are lined up in neat rows.

General Electric

heat out lengthwise, the electronic gear feels practically no change in heat at all. In the same way, a long channel of pyrographite can conduct electricity more efficiently than ordinary graphite. This pyrographite could be used for much better carbon electrodes, in a great many cases from electric furnaces to welding machines.

The above is just one "trick" that can be performed with the ordering of materials. The crystal structure might be built in any number of ways to give different effects. For instance, it might be assembled to pass heat easily from top to bottom and oppose it end-to-end. There are also other pyrolytic materials → pyrolytic boron nitride ceramic, for example — being studied with different properties and advantages than graphite.

Many studies are being made of the action of atoms under temperature extremes. Unique approaches have been developed to study the inner motion of materials. One example is a mechanical model invented by General Electric scientists. This device makes use of small glass beads and a vibrating glass plate to simulate the motion of atoms.

The beads are poured onto a round glass plate with a railing around it to keep the beads from rolling off. The plate is suspended from springs and is vibrated constantly by a motor underneath. The beads take on a pattern of motion similar to that which atoms are believed to follow. As Dr. David Turnbull of General Electric Research Laboratories states, "The properties of matter result from the interaction of many atoms. The long-range goal of material science is to calculate these interactions and thus predict the behavior of matter. However, precise calculations are very difficult and models can be of use by suggesting how such calculations may be simplified."

This model can be used to simulate the atomic movement of all types of matter, from gases to liquids. For instance, when only a few beads are present on the table, says Turnbull, they behave like atoms in a gas, moving rapidly over long distances between collisions and arranging themselves in no particular pattern. As more and more beads are added, the group behaves like a liquid. Eventually, when the tray is filled with beads, they act like a solid, forming several large areas separated by the equivalent of grain boundaries. Temperature effects in a model such as this can be made by changing the amount of vibration. The effect of an increase in temperature on real atoms is to make them move faster and faster. Decreasing temperature usually makes the atoms move more sluggishly.

Of course, this is just one rather simple tool used in the study of basic structure. Many other kinds of equipment, both simple and complex, are used at laboratories throughout the country. One result of such studies has been the uncovering of a whole new and very promising technology of materials at very low temperatures. This is the field known as *superconductivity.*

Superconductivity is again not new. It was discovered by the European scientist Kammerligh Omnes in 1911. But it has only been in the past few years that widespread research on the basic effects of low temperatures on the properties of materials has led to important practical possibilities. What is superconductivity? The word refers to the electrical properties of materials. Normally, when an electric current flows in a wire, it is opposed by a property of the material known as *resistance*. This means that to keep an electric current flowing in a wire, there must be some kind of electric pump such as a battery constantly forcing the current to flow. Otherwise the wire resistance will soon stop the current movement.

In 1911, though, Omnes discovered that a very strange thing happened to Mercury when its temperature was lowered to about minus 453 degrees Fahrenheit. At this temperature, mercury's resistance seemed to completely disappear. Later tests, particularly work done in the past few years, have shown that the same thing happens to a number of other metals and compounds at low temperatures. A material with zero resistance to the flow of electricity is said to be superconducting. It might also be pointed out that many materials will not become superconducting no matter how much their temperature is lowered. Some of the elements that can be made superconducting are aluminum, tin, vanadium, zirconium, columbium, molybdenum, lead, uranium, zinc, and many of the rare earths.

Among the superconducting compounds, a very interesting series is the group of materials called *intermetallics*. One superconductor is an intermetallic combination of columbium and tin. However, the way metals go together in intermetallics is not the same as the way metallic elements combine in a *metal alloy*. The intermetallics are compounds where the metals are bonded together rather than mixed as in an alloy, just as hydrogen and oxygen make the compound called water. Thus the intermetallic has properties very different from a metal, just as water is much different from the two gases of which it is formed. Intermetallics act like ceramics and usually are considered part of the ceramic family.

This again indicates the continuing need for development of materials as a science. The important things scientists want to know about intermetallics and superconductors in general is not whether they are metals or ceramics, but how they act under certain conditions, such as extremely low temperatures.

To get back to the highly important meaning of superconductivity, Battelle scientists point out that this potentially is one of the greatest advances of the century. Let's say we have a superconductive wire and an electric current is induced in it. Since the wire has no resistance, once this current is started it will flow for years, theoretically forver, without any outside aid. In most present-day electrical systems, a good part of the equipment is there just to keep the current flowing against system resistance. In a superconductive system, this pumping system can be eliminated, permitting the design of very small, compact electrical units for many applications.

An example of this, already being studied on a laboratory scale, is a computer only a few inches square that can do the job of a present-day computer that takes up the whole side of a room. It might also be possible to install in a small area of the basement all the electrical equipment needed to light a private home and run household appliances. No longer would the homeowner need to worry about storms destroying power lines and leaving him without electricity.

Intermetallics offer other properties for superconductivity of even wider potential. The columbium-tin intermetallic mentioned above has been found to be superconductive in such a way that it lets scientists generate very high magnetic fields. In chapter seven, the great promise of nuclear fusion was pointed out as well as the chief problem. The problem is to generate the extremely powerful magnetic fields needed to "pinch" atoms of hydrogen together. Conventional magnets tend to tear themselves apart mainly because of resistance. The greater the magnetic force needed, the greater is the material resistance encountered. Eventually something has to give and it is the magnet material which fails. However, if there is no resistance, it is relatively easy to get larger and larger magnetic fields. A magnet made with the columbium-tin material can produce a magnetic field seven to ten times as great as the most powerful ever created before. There is also the chance that an even newer intermetallic, vanadium-gallium, would make it possible to develop a magnet more than seven times as powerful as that made with columbium-tin.

If progress with superconductivity continues, it may be possible to achieve practical nuclear fusion with relatively small units. As Dr. Malcolm Currie of Hughes Aircraft's Research and Development Laboratories points out, practical superconductivity would make it possible to build high-performance, lightweight nuclear space engines. Fusion engines would provide enough power so that pilots could maneuver spaceships as easily as they now fly aircraft.

As promising as superconductivity may be — and some superconducting materials are already in use in certain kinds of military electronic equipment — universal use is still some years or even decades away. The difficulty in obtaining the very low temperatures required for superconductivity is the major stumbling block. Special kinds of refrigerators are needed to produce temperatures several hundred degrees below zero. These temperatures, after all, are many times lower than those maintained by the household food freezers. At present, refrigeration units which can produce such low temperatures are bulky and fragile. For use in home superconducting units or aboard nuclear spaceships, the low-temperature refrigerators must be smaller and more efficient than those of today. More years of study will be required before superconductivity will be practical in the home.

A little closer to completion are the studies that will

make possible radios the size of pinheads, such as those mentioned at the beginning of this chapter. This is the area of tailored materials research known as *thin-film* technology. Thin-film work developed from studies of transistors and other small electronic devices called *solid-state* parts. In the electronic industry, solid-state means parts made of solid materials rather than glass vacuum tubes.

All recent progress in electronics is based on understanding the ways in which electrons move in solid materials. This knowledge will be equally important in the future. In the 1950s, scientists found that using the movement of electrons in and out of solids could give the same effects gained in large electrical equipment. The difference was that solid-state units were much smaller. The result was the pocket-size transistor radios, small portable television sets, more efficient automobile ignition systems, and other small, durable pieces of electronic equipment.

The motion of electrons in solids in such devices as the transistor is based on the use of "donor" and "acceptor" atoms. Let's see how this works with germanium. The germanium atom has four electrons in its outer shell, each of which can form bonds with an electron on another germanium atom. Now another kind of atom, called an "impurity," is introduced into the germanium crystal. Let's say the new atom is arsenic. Arsenic has five lectrons in its outer shell. Four of these form bonds with germanium atoms. The fifth can make no bond and thus can easily be broken loose.

This kind of atom is called a "donor" since it gives free electrons to the circuit.

Now let's say a different kind of impurity, such as indium, is introduced into a different section of the germanium crystal. Indium only has three electrons in its outer orbit. These three join with three germanium electrons but the fourth position is open. This void is called a "hole" and this kind of atom an "acceptor."

If a current is then induced in the material by, say, a battery, electrons break away from the donors and flow into the holes in the acceptors. One battery terminal attracts electrons from the acceptors, opening new holes while other electrons flow into the germanium from the other battery terminal. Thus a steady flow of electrons through the circuit is set up. The amounts of impurities that have been introduced into the germanium determine what the strength and nature of the transistor output will be.

Scientists later discovered that even small modern electronic systems could be made more efficient by eliminating the bulky connections which tied the parts of a system together.

Materials for better, smaller transistors also were created. In both cases the size of parts was reduced by thin-film technology.

Special chemical methods of depositing layers of material millionths of an inch thick on special *wafer* bases were invented. One way this is done is by a process known as *vapor deposition*. First, the very small base material, usually a very thin wafer of plastic or a glass compound, is placed in a special chamber. The materials to be plated on the wafer are then introduced into this chamber as fine vapors suspended in a gas. As the gas passes over the wafer, a very thin film of the vaporized material coats the wafer. The film may be only an atom or two in thickness.

A series of coatings may be deposited on the wafer in this way. Each coating can be of a different material with different properties. For instance, the first coat might be a layer of transistor material, such as silicon. After the transistor material a layer of aluminum or copper might be the next coat on the wafer. This second coat serves the same purpose in the tiny device that a wire would in a large piece of equipment. Then the wafer might receive coatings of other materials with still other properties. The end product is a very tiny device that can do the same job that is done by a large piece of electronic gear with tubes, bulky resistors, and wiring.

The reason the tiny device can do the same job as the large one is that thin films permit the most efficient use of the atomic properties of matter. Much of the materials used in the larger piece of electronic equipment is wasted because conventional production methods require the use of large parts for ease of handling. Technicians assembling the parts must work with such relatively clumsy tools as soldering irons and screw drivers. With thin film it is possible to use almost exactly the number of atoms necessary to perform a particular electronic operation in the place where the

Autonetics

Scientist adjusts laboratory gear used in making molecular (extremely small) electronic equipment. In this tubing, thin layers of special electronic material are deposited on very small silicon-base wafers.

material can perform the job most efficiently.

The efficient use of atoms can also provide much better performance in conventional equipment such as

Miniature amplifier, the result of tailored materials research, takes the place of an electronic device previously larger than the pages of this book.

television sets. The special coating called a phosphor used on the inside of a television tube is sensitive to streams of electrons which are sent against it by an electron gun at the other end of the tube. The phosphor glows with different amounts of light depending on the number of electrons and the way they hit its surface. The combination of light and darker areas forms the picture.

Present-day phosphors are painted on the tubes in the form of relatively thick powders. The crystals of these powders are not arranged in any particular order. Often these crystals lie in such a way that they waste light by reflecting the light backwards instead of towards the viewing side of the tube. This action limits the resolution, or picture sharpness, of the television tube. By coating tubes with thin-film phosphors it is possible to obtain a carefully arranged atomic structure with little reflection. A thin film coat for television tubes which has been tested recently produces a television picture fifteen times sharper than present-day coatings. This coating may be used in only a few years.

A step beyond thin-film technique is the field of molecular electronics. Researchers in molecular electronics are attempting to create complete electronic devices in a single piece of material by changing the relationship of parts of the atomic or molecular structure of the material. For example, in research work sponsored by the U.S. Air Force at Westinghouse Electric, ribbons of a single crystal electronic material, such as germanium or silicon, are being grown. As the ribbons move along a tiny assembly line, sections of the crystals are treated with different kinds of impurities to form such things as amplifiers or radio receivers.

Forgetting about the names of different materials, consider what has been pointed out throughout this book. Atoms are atoms. They will act in different ways depending on the conditions to which they are exposed. Little groups of impurities change the atomic structure of the base material in various ways, depending on how the impurities are placed in the base. The result is that the same base material can be made to act like an electronic switch in one place or a current

Westinghouse

Molecular materials studies at Westinghouse Electric Research Labs led to making the button held by the girl to take the place of the amplifier unit shown on the table.

conductor in another. Thus, a very small strip of material can be treated with impurities and it will become a complete electronic device in an all-but-invisible package.

There are many problems in doing this, but they

will be solved. It's a slow process to learn just how to arrange the atoms to do the various jobs. Also, it's one thing to make one or two special circuits in the laboratory and quite another to mass-produce hundreds or thousands cheaply and reliably. In any case, striking gains have been made in research tests, and these tests will lead to many amazing new things for tomorrow's home and industry.

One example of a device for tomorrow has been shown by Westinghouse Electric scientists. It is a microminiature amplifier system for a high fidelity phonograph. The part of the system known as the pre-amplifier is the size of a match head and the power amplifier is smaller than a dime. The phonograph plays normal phonograph records, but the devices which furnish power to run the phonograph are difficult to find without a magnifying glass. "If this can be accomplished now," says Westinghouse's Dr. G. C. Sziklai, "it isn't difficult to foresee a complete communications receiver the size of a pea within a few years."

10

MATERIALS IN THE
WORLD OF TOMORROW

"THE FUTURE IS getting here much sooner than it used to," is the way the trend of technology has been described by some materials experts. The bewildering advances in new materials research have been described in preceding chapters. Can we then imagine what all these developments will mean in the world of tomorrow?

Obviously the answer is yes. With few exceptions, we can think of inventions that seem impossible today and be almost certain that future generations will see these "impossibilities" become reality. The new science of materials is moving ahead so fast that many of these predictions may become fact almost before the ink has dried on these pages.

Many of us have wished for window glass that would take a blow from a baseball without breaking. The same wish for break-proof glass has been made silently by many a housewife after seeing a beautiful

New Chemcor glass developed by Corning Glass Works can be bent, twisted, dropped without breaking.

and valuable vase or goblet shatter into a thousand pieces on the floor. Just a year or two ago, this kind of wishing would have seemed useless. At best, break-proof glass was thought to be a development which was far in the future. But it's here, in its early stages, today. Corning Glass Corporation has introduced chemically treated Chemcor glass that is five times stronger than the best glass available in the past. Completely transparent pieces of this glass have been made so tough they can be bent back and forth and twisted without so much as a crack. With this as a beginning, we can see the end to all the problems that go with the brittle glass we now know.

Conceivably, it may become a simple thing to make tremendous glass domes to enclose complete cities. This development would make it possible to colonize other planets which have atmospheres man cannot breathe. In the depths of the sea, glass-domed cities with artificial sunlight could house miners of the great mineral wealth we know is stored in the ocean floor. Also, the ocean is a great future source of food, and the ocean-farmers of tomorrow might also have their glass-domed domains.

The advanced materials of the past few years — in particular the many synthetic plastics — have already made great changes in the clothing we wear. Combined materials of the future will make possible a choice of inexpensive, lightweight clothing for any climate. Some of these garments probably will have their own automatic temperature-humidity controls. The moment the climate around the wearer changes, these controls will adjust the atomic structure of the clothing for maximum comfort.

Going one step further, the materials of tomorrow may well make throwaway clothing a reality. Just as today we have disposable paper and plastic cups, plates, and spoons, soon we may have shirts, blouses, and undergarments that can be worn once or perhaps a few times, then discarded. This might sound like tremendous wastage, but once we know the secrets of the atomic structure of all materials, it could be possible to have a never-ending cycle of clothing use, disposal, and reuse.

For instance, the used material could be thrown into a special collection device. All the clothing could then be conveyed to a central plant that would break down the materials to their basic elements. These elements could then be fed back into clothing manufacturing machines to be made into new disposable clothing. This approach might make obsolete all home washing, but it's doubtful that any mothers or housekeepers would protest very much.

Of course, for those who love beautiful materials and who like to preserve them, materials technology also can make possible the direct opposite of throwaway clothes. It is obvious that we are learning enough about the nature of materials to make textiles and other kinds of flexible materials that can last for centuries. These materials will last despite all kinds of extreme wear and tear. Clothing, rugs, drapes of this future fabric will repel dirt and staining or destructive fluids. Some textiles may be self-healing so that they could be ripped with a knife and repaired just by pressing the cut edges together.

Communications, of course, will be not only worldwide, but interplanetary. The Telstar communications satellite which linked Europe and the United States in worldwide television coverage is just the first crude step towards this goal. Many of the advances discussed in this book — thin-film electronics, superconductivity, ultrasound — will make possible a lightweight, portable telephone which can be carried in a pocket. Such telephones would enable the user to call his home from his car, his office, in London, Paris, or even on the Moon. Television of tomorrow will show "live" travelogues of the surface of Mars, Venus, and the other planets. Naturally, full-color television will be available at very low cost. In addition, some form of three-dimensional television will be used. It might be possible to have a stage show given in one central theater and have it reproduced in three dimensions on full-size stages in other theaters throughout the country.

The revolution in communications will extend to our daily papers. Dr. L. V. Berkner, head of Southwest Research Institute, in his communications lecture at Lincoln Laboratory, Massachusetts Institute of Technology, pointed to the progress already made toward printing of newspapers in many different cities simultaneously. *The New York Times* recently started a Los Angeles daily edition. The electronic methods of today make it possible to tie together typesetting machines in the two cities. When one machine in New York sets type for the paper, it automatically operates the machine in Los Angeles. The same newspapers thus can be printed anywhere in the United States at the same time. In the future this can be done on a worldwide basis. In addition, the newspapers of tomorrow will look more like the slick magazines of today, for color methods and costs will be lowered to the point that full-color newspapers will be run off every day.

The combined development of super-strong materials and ever smaller electronic and mechanical equipment will also make possible even more striking advances in transportation than anything we have seen in the jet age. By the 1970s, regularly scheduled airliners will fly at more than three times the speed of sound. Plans for aircraft of the 1980s are under study. These planes will travel at Mach 7 or about 5,000 miles per hour.

At the same time, prospects seem bright for combination plane-cars to replace today's earth-bound automobiles. Electronic devices will make such vehicles so safe that the average person will be able to fly from one place to another without danger. As time goes on, development of the small plane-car will probably lead to small private spacecraft for more daring citizens.

For all of us, the homes of tomorrow will be much easier to care for and to build. Tomorrow's homes will also be better lighted and more attractive. There was a time when it was thought that only metals could conduct electric current. Then, as noted earlier in this book, scientists found that such non-metals as silicon or silicon carbide could be used. This led to development of transistors and other modern electronic parts. Still, it didn't seem likely that such materials as plastics or glass could ever be used to conduct current. These normally are insulators and are used to keep current from leaking out of a conductor. Once again, however, research showed that some kinds of plastic could be made that would carry electricity.

New materials such as these made it possible to develop the idea of electroluminescence. The approach is already being used for back-lighting, or providing a soft glow so instrument panels can be read in the dark. Instrument panels on some types of advanced missiles and aircraft are back-lighted. When applied to the home or factory, back-lighting produces a more even distribution of light through a room. The homeowner of the future will be able to get light just where he wants it by adjusting certain controls.

It will be possible to "paint" with light by making different parts of a room glow with varying light patterns in different colors. Another aspect of electroluminescence is that varying the electrical levels in a wall will permit changing one area so that it is opaque and another so it is transparent. This will permit the homeowner to move his windows to any location and size any time he wants to. In addition, these windows can be made to permit him to look out while preventing anyone from looking.

The houses of tomorrow will also be of much stronger, lighter building materials. In addition, the air conditioning system which will be custom-built into every home or apartment will automatically screen out all particles of dirt or dust. This will eliminate the need for vacuum cleaning or dusting. In many cases, the materials used in a house will come painted in the owner's choice of colors. Where paint must be applied, it will not crack or peel. Also, paints will be available that will be just about permanent, with just a hosing down needed to clean them and restore their bright colors.

We can already see the way to ending the problems of faulty plumbing. Self-sealing valve and gasket materials, forerunners of which are now being used in advanced missiles and spacecraft, will make leaky faucets a thing of the past. Metal pipe which rusts and corrodes will be replaced by non-metallic pipe. Within ten to twenty years strong plastic pipes will be used both in home and city installations. Plastic, of course, isn't rusted away by water the way much of today's plumbing is. This will mean that pipe leaks will no longer be a problem and we will no longer find rust in our drinking water when the water system has not been used for a while.

In the field of health, we have already seen in the chapter on plastics how basic polymer research will lead to even greater strides in the war against disease. Materials of all kinds will also be devised that will be essentially germ-free to prevent the spread of disease germs. Certainly it seems inevitable that compounds will be found to eliminate many of the viruses that cause many of our less dangerous but annoying ailments.

One of the problems highlighted in recent years has

been the possible harmful effects of certain chemicals and insecticides on man. There's no doubt that as we gain a better understanding of materials, it will be possible to replace any dangerous germ or insect killer with safe, yet effective, compounds.

As scientists learn more about the basic nature of materials they will be able to develop synthetic skin and body parts. From a storehouse of such parts, it will be possible to rapidly repair most damage by grafting new tissues or body organs in place. Some of the first steps have already begun. For example, a recent government research report notes that a new kind of plastic has been made which can be used to help mend broken bones.

The development of special materials for advanced electronic systems also is leading to the invention of special miniature medical instruments that can be inserted inside the body. For instance, miniature television camera probes will be used so doctors can see exactly what has gone wrong when a patient complains of internal pain. The use of other very small instruments in addition to internal television will make it possible for surgeons of the future to operate right at the trouble spot rather than cutting through healthy portions of skin and tissue to reach a diseased or damaged area. Another side of medicine of the future is diagnosis by computer. Today, diagnosis of illness depends upon the physician's experience. This means the doctor must have observed similar symptoms in other patients or perhaps he recalls what he has read in medical books and journals. As continued advances in materials technology make smaller, less expensive computers possible, every family doctor will be able to have his own office computer. He can feed a list of a patient's symptoms into the machine and in minutes obtain a diagnosis based on cases stored in the very accurate computer memory. The computer will be a valuable aid to the doctor's own observation and experience.

Aside from medicine, computers will play a large part in many other areas of life in the future. We have discussed how low-temperature technology is making it possible to build computers which are only a few inches square. Such small computers someday may be made inexpensive enough to be used in the home. Families will then be able to figure their household budgets in a few minutes by feeding the information into a home computer. Banks and factories, of course, already make use of computer systems. In banks, computers automatically control and speed up many book-keeping operations. In factories, computers operate assembly lines and many complex tools. In the future, computers in the bank teller's cage will cut waiting time for depositors. Computer controls for the automobiles of tomorrow will maintain a car's highway speed without the driver having to touch the controls. These units also will slow the car to automatically avoid obstacles and stop the car completely in dangerous situations. Advances such as these can finally eliminate the great number of highway deaths that occur every year.

With the population explosion continuing to out-pace food production in much of the world, we must look to materials research to help solve the world's food problem. At present, all signs are that a technology is coming into being to accomplish this. Stanford Research Institute scientists note that current research in polymers and combined materials indicates it will be possible to make special soil stabilizers to control soil erosion by water and wind. This would stop the tragic loss of farmland which plagues much of the world.

Combined with soil stabilization would be development of fertilizers which would release food to the growing plants only as the plants need it. Researchers say that production of stronger and cheaper glazing and shading materials will make it possible to have closer control over growing conditions in large areas of the earth. Great stretches of low-cost, lightweight shades could be built to cover entire farms. These shades could then be adjusted to allow the plants the right amount of sunlight for good crop growth.

Still another important innovation for farming is development of inexpensive, strong, weather-resistant pipe and pumping systems for irrigation. These materials for irrigation systems would make it possible to undertake bigger irrigation projects and reclaim waste lands. Combined with perfection of methods to get fresh water from sea water, advanced irrigation systems will finally let man realize the dream of reconquering the world's deserts.

Of course, to make such systems work requires a great deal of power. Nuclear energy is one possible answer, but still others are on the horizon, including solar energy and fuel cells. In recent years, scientists have developed special silicon solar cells for spacecraft. These, of course, take energy from the sun and convert it to electricity to run the electrical equipment on board the vehicle. One goal of materials researchers is to gain much greater cell efficiency. Today's cells turn only about ten per cent of the sunlight that hits them into useful energy. When solar cells become more efficient, arrays of them can be used in remote areas to furnish electricity for farm equipment, irrigation systems, lighting, and telephones.

One of the most promising energy sources for the future is the fuel cell. Advanced materials research has shown that special combinations of materials can be used to build self-charging batteries. These batteries produce energy directly from chemical energy fed to them. Today's batteries operate on certain amounts of material that are slowly used up. In the fuel cell, a constant flow of new fuel is fed into the cell. This fuel can be a mixture of such gases as carbon and oxygen.

Since the fuel is relatively cheap and might even be extracted from the air, small batteries of this type could be used for ten years or more without wearing out. Certainly batteries that almost never wear out will be important in the world of tomorrow. Fuel cells are already being used on some of our satellites, and the day is coming when these cells will be used in battery-operated trucks and cars, completely portable electric barbecues, and many other products.

In food technology, much more will obviously come to pass from the invention of synthetic foods and encouragement of efficient plant growth. Still another area in which advances will occur is the use of atomic materials to irradiate food. Preliminary work has shown that exposing certain kinds of food to carefully controlled amounts of radiation can be accomplished without harm to the food or eventual consumer. What irradiation does is destroy the germs that normally cause decay in foods. Irradiated food can then be kept on kitchen shelves for months and perhaps years without spoiling.

Of course, irradiated foods cannot be exposed to the air. After irradiation, they are packaged in a special wrapper. After the wrapper is removed, the normal decay of food will take place.

Naturally, not all foods can be successfully irradiated and some refrigeration will probably always be needed. But meat and many fruits and vegetables can be treated in this way in the future so they can just be stacked in the open until they're needed.

There will be continued increases in the use of energy in what we now might consider unusual forms. Sound waves, for instance, are presently being used for welding hard-to-weld materials. In addition, sound waves in the form of ultrasonic energy are serving many other functions. One of these is in "nondestructive testing." This is a way of testing a material without having to ruin it. By passing very high frequency sound waves through a part, it is possible to detect the smallest flaw or weakness inside the material. In the future, ultrasonics will also be used for such different things as manufacturing improved metals and ceramics, and cooking without heat.

Light waves also are being used for many new things today. Special electronic equipment using light waves is needed to make communications over the vast distances of space possible. As has been mentioned earlier, special high-energy light-beam producers known as lasers are used for this and also for effective welding and machining of certain materials.

Perhaps the most amazing use of light which will come in the future is as energy for space propulsion. The development of nuclear space engines will make manned journeys to all the planets of our solar system a reality. However, the distances to the stars are so great that even nuclear engines would not provide enough power. The only answer scientists now see is the use of the tremendous energies potentially available in light waves. Called photon propulsion, this type of power is the main hope of the future for sending exploratory probes to the far-off stars. Photon propulsion is not something you or I or our children will see come to pass. However, it seems certain that in coming centuries it will carry the revolution of space travel to the farthest depths of the universe.

These are just a few glimpses of materials in the world of tomorrow. Obviously, it is possible to solve the physical problems of our world and also extend our exploration of space as our scientific progress continues. If our use of this great knowledge is wise, the world of the future may be even more fantastic than any predictions made here.

RELATIVE ABUNDANCE OF THE ELEMENTS
IN COMMON ROCK

ABUNDANCE	ATOMIC NUMBER	ELEMENT	ABUNDANCE	ATOMIC NUMBER	ELEMENT
296	8	O	0.00095	32	Ge
100	14	Si	0.0008	82	Pb
30.5	13	Al	0.00067	33	As
12.4	11	Na	0.00053	55	Cs
9.17	20	Ca	0.0005	90	Th
9.13	26	Fe	0.000419	62	Sm
8.76	12	Mg	0.000394	64	Gd
4.42	19	K	0.000389	59	Pr
			0.0003	72	Hf
0.92	22	Ti	0.000269	66	Dy
0.32-0.48	9	F	0.0002	35	Br
0.38	15	P	0.00016	92	U
0.27	6	C	0.000149	70	Yb
0.18	25	Mn	0.000144	68	Er
0.16	16	S	0.00012	73	Ta
0.09	17	Cl	0.000083	51	Sb
0.039	24	Cr	0.000082	74	W
0.036	37	Rb	0.000068	63	Eu
0.035	38	Sr	0.000068	67	Ho
0.033	7	N	0.000056	65	Tb
0.03	23	V	0.000037	71	Lu
0.026	40	Zr	0.000024	53	I
0.02	30	Zn	0.000015	81	Tl
0.018	56	Ba	0.0000115	69	Tm
0.014	28	Ni			
0.011	29	Cu	9.0×10^{-6}	83	Bi
			7.6 "	2	He
0.0067	4	Be	$3.9\text{-}3.925 \times 10^{-6}$	80	Hg
0.004	27	Co			
0.00343	50	Sn	2.7×10^{-7}	78	Pt
0.00321	58	Ce	2.6 "	79	Au
0.00301	39	Y			
0.0028	5	B	5.4×10^{-8}	75	Re
0.0026	41	Nb	5 "	77	Ir
0.0022	31	Ga	5.8×10^{-12}	88	Ra
0.00162	60	Nd	3.5 "	91	Pa
0.00128	57	La	1.4×10^{-15}	84	Po
			1.3 "	89	Ac

Table from K. Rankama and T. G. Sahama, "Geochemistry," Univ. of Chicago Press, 1951. The table presents the elements in order of decreasing atomic abundance, based on the number of silicon atoms being equal to 100. It is based on the analysis of the number of atoms of each element present in common rocks of the earth's surface. It indicates how few elements actually make up most of our planet's surface.

To save space, the last 11 elements' abundance are given in mathematical shorthand. The minus number over the 10 indicates the whole number at the left is that number of places from the decimal. Thus 9.0×10^{-6} means the nine is the sixth position from the decimal or: 0.000009.

GLOSSARY OF
CHEMICAL ABBREVIATIONS
For Table on Preceding Page

O	Oxygen	Ge	Germanium
Si	Silicon	Pb	Lead
Al	Aluminum	As	Arsenic
Na	Sodium	Cs	Cesium
Ca	Calcium	Th	Thorium
Fe	Iron	Sm	Samarium
Mg	Magnesium	Gd	Gadolinium
K	Potassium	Pr	Praseodymium
Ti	Titanium	Hf	Hafnium
F	Fluorine	Dy	Dysprosium
P	Phosphorus	Br	Bromine
C	Carbon	U	Uranium
Mn	Manganese	Yb	Ytterbium
S	Sulphur	Er	Erbium
Cl	Chlorine	Ta	Tantalum
Cr	Chromium	Sb	Antimony
Rb	Rubidium	W	Tungsten
Sr	Strontium	Eu	Europium
N	Nitrogen	Ho	Holmium
V	Vanadium	Tb	Terbium
Zr	Zirconium	Lu	Lutecium
Zn	Zinc	I	Iodine
Ba	Barium	Tl	Thallium
Ni	Nickel	Tm	Thulium
Cu	Copper	Bi	Bismuth
Be	Beryllium	He	Helium
Co	Cobalt	Hg	Mercury
Sn	Stannum (Tin)	Pt	Platinum
Ce	Cerium	Au	Gold
Y	Yttrium	Re	Rhenium
B	Boron	Ir	Iridium
Nb	Niobium	Ra	Radium
Ga	Gallium	Pa	Protactinium
Nd	Neodymium	Po	Polonium
La	Lanthanum	Ac	Actinium

INDEX

INDEX

THE AUTHOR

IRWIN STAMBLER received his degree in aeronautical engineering from New York University and worked for a number of years in the aviation industry. At the same time he lists as one of his most unusual jobs that of "toy buster" for a large department store's bureau of standards. It was his task to apply his engineering skills to testing the durability of toys sold by the store.

As an engineer he was aware of the need for clear and concise reports and found he could handle such work well. He extended this ability to include magazine stories and articles, eventually combining engineering and writing to become Materials Editor of *Space/Aeronautics,* a leading trade journal for the aviation and space industry. Mr. Stambler's principal job is to keep himself and his readers informed of the latest developments in the science of materials.

Build the Unknown came naturally from his current work and a special interest in writing about scientific subjects for young readers. His other books include *Space Ship: The Story of X-15; Find a Career in Aviation; Find a Career in Engineering; Wonders of Underwater Exploration* and *Breath of Life,* the story of modern exploration of our atmosphere. In addition he has written for adult readers *The Battle for Inner Space,* a survey of undersea exploration.

Mr. Stambler lives with his wife and four children in Redondo Beach, California.